BRAIN TRUST

ALSO BY GARTH SUNDEM

The Geeks' Guide to World Domination

Brain Candy

93 Top Scientists
Reveal Lab-Tested Secrets to
Surfing, Dating, Dieting, Gambling, Growing Man-Eating Plants, and More!

BRAIN TRUST

GARTH SUNDEM

THREE RIVERS PRESS
NEW YORK

Published in the United States by Three Rivers Press, an imprint of the Crown Publishing Group, a division of Penguin Random House LLC, New York.
www.crownpublishing.com

Three Rivers Press and the Tugboat design are registered trademarks of Penguin Random House LLC.

Originally published in the United States by Three Rivers Press, an imprint of the Crown Publishing Group, a division of Penguin Random House LLC, New York, in 2012.

Library of Congress Cataloging-in-Publication Data

Sundem, Garth.
Brain Trust: 93 top scientists reveal lab-tested secrets to surfing, dating, dieting, gambling, growing man-eating plants, and more! / Garth Sundem.
p. cm.

Summary: "Based entirely on original interviews with Nobel laureates, MacArthur geniuses, National Science Medal winners, and other leading scientists, *Brain Trust* delivers more than 100 proven, scientifically valid tips guaranteed to make you more awesome"—Provided by publisher.
Science—Miscellanea. 1. Title.
Q173.S947 2012
500-dc23
2011022036

ISBN 978-0-385-36526-0

Printed in the United States of America

Book design: Maria Elias
Illustrations: Garth Sundem
Cover design: Kyle Kolker
Cover photographs: (shirt) © Brand X Pictures; (scientists) Lambert/Archive Photos/Getty Images

1 3 5 7 9 10 8 6 4 2

To the 130-ish brilliant scientists who took time
from teaching, research, and their otherwise busy lives
to tutor me in how to best live mine.

CONTENTS

INTRODUCTION

When you open the passenger-side door of my car, one of the following things tends to fall out: a kid's shoe, a water bottle, or a once-coveted stick, pinecone, acorn, large leaf, pill bug, or rock. On special occasions it'll be an In-N-Out french fry. Once it was a favorite running sock I'd been missing for months.

I had ample opportunity to note these ejaculations every morning as I jumped into the passenger seat with my laptop and cell phone to do the interviews for this book.

You see, the car's messy, but the garage is also the quietest place in my house. In the background of the first interviews I did, before stumbling onto the soundproof powers of Subaru, you can hear my "extremely fierce" Labrador protecting the house from things like early-rising birds and people in hats jogging past (joggers with bare heads are fine—who can know the mind of a Labrador?). Or you can hear me saying to my four-year-old, "Hey, good morning, buddy! Go jump in bed with Mom." I've put some of the recordings online at garthsundem.com—they're worth a chuckle.

I can't tell if talking to Nobel Laureates, MacArthur geniuses, National Medal of Science winners, and the like while hiding in the garage is empowering, embarrassing, or just odd in the manner of the proverbial mom with her hair in rollers pretending to be a nymph while talking dirty for a 1-900 service.

Anyway.

This book is what happens when science hits life. It gets messy.

And when you get off the script that some of these top-notch scientists have perfected over years of keynotes, classes, invited lectures, and interviews with people sitting at actual desks, you find that scientists are messy too. You hear the story of psychologist Stephen Greenspan's initiation into the science of gullibility when his mother duped him into marrying his then girlfriend. Or about mathematician Ian Stewart's wife trying to use rotational mechanics to teach their malfunctioning cat to land on its feet. You get to listen to statistician Wayne Winston yelling at USA basketball while on the phone because his model predicted a wider point spread. You hear about how MIT prosthetics researcher Hugh Herr replaced his lost legs with DIY feet to climb some of the most difficult rock faces in the world, or how physicist Charles Edmondson used the geometry of roadways to chase down a turbo Porsche with a lowly Dodge Neon.

It turns out that the root of today's best science is the passenger seat of scientists' messy cars. In other words, the science in this book comes from the very real experiences and problems of scientists' own lives.

And rather than ice-eyed intellectuals perched in ivory towers (as their precisely worded papers might imply), it turns out that scientists are passionate, excited, and bubbly about their specialties to the point of schoolgirls with Justin Bieber infatuations. (You should hear the utterly awesome Steve Strogatz talk about crickets, bridges, and his high school calculus teacher.) Get a scientist talking about her search for discovery and it starts to sound like a page-turning adventure book, which is exactly what I hope this book has turned out to be.

That said, don't let the glib delivery lull you into thinking this is puff pastry. This book is supposed to be fun and practical, but it's also one of the most info-dense entities in the known universe ($I = mc^2$).

OK, maybe that's a tiny bit of an exaggeration. But if you slow down, maybe hang your head out the window like the aforementioned Labrador, you'll find that the one hundred–some bite-sized bugs of how-to science stuck in your teeth in fact represent whole fields of cutting-edge research.

I loved writing this book—who gets to wear boxer shorts and drink Sumatra blend in the passenger seat of a parked Outback while chatting with Steven Pinker about how to bribe a cop? But the truth is, talking to sometimes three or four Nobel, MacArthur, and National Medal of Science winners in a morning nearly drove me batty.

You see, in addition to being overwhelmingly brilliant and passionate, it's a fair stereotype to note that each scientific field tends to either attract or create people with its own brand of quirks. For example, computer science professors respond to e-mails immediately or not at all. Physicists almost always have a serious side interest in basketball or race cars or sailing or card tricks or the like. (Thank you, Richard Feynman?) Social psychologists are happy to talk off the cuff, but are very concerned about being misquoted. Mathematicians tended to seem a bit surprised I would get in touch, were likely to tentatively dip a toe into the conversation, but then if I understood anything at all in the first five minutes, would ramble happily and fascinatingly for hours. Economists were sure to point out that their theoretical work is borne out in the real world, and biologists and anthropologists were sure to point out that their field observations are replicable in the lab.

Amid 130-ish interviews, it was hard to avoid jumping on the quirk train myself. For example, after a week spent mining a particularly deep vein of behavioral economists and applied mathematicians, I found myself charting my car's passenger-door ejections from one day to the next, hoping to glean some sort of great statistically predictive insight. When might the great oracle my family has affectionately nicknamed Zippy the Wonder Tank return my other running sock?

In fact, with my brain now addled by ricocheting thoughts born of that special leading edge where science meets fiction, I can't seem to stop mishmashing together my messy life with the work of these scientists.

I wonder about the pigeons that splinter off from the flock that circles the street by my house every night at sunset. I wonder if Cliff Lee should still throw heat to a batter who specializes in hitting fastballs. I wonder how I should best list ride-on-top toys on eBay to encourage rabid bidding. I wonder why the Ping-Pong balls my kids race in gutters on rainy days tend to stick together like Cheerios in a bowl. I start charting the detritus that falls out of my car. . . .

Yes, this book will teach you how to improve your life with science. You'll learn tricks for dieting better, dating better, driving better, and betting better. You'll learn how to get better odds from the lottery, you'll learn how to learn, and avoid car theft, and win poker, and get away with crimes in broad daylight. But I hope by the end, rather than having all your questions answered, you find yourself wandering around as totally wonder-struck as I am: With a bike and a bus pass, what's the most efficient way to visit every bakery in this city? Am I more likely to get hit with pigeon poop or find a twenty-dollar bill? Should I wait or circle to find a parking spot in this busy lot? What in the small space between my Labrador's ears makes him distrust people in hats?

Life is messy, and starting to pick it apart with science shows you just how brilliant and wild and interconnected and fascinating it is.

It's a good messy.

BRAIN TRUST

TRANSFORM A RELATIONSHIP WITH LANGUAGE

Steven Pinker COGNITIVE SCIENCE, HARVARD UNIVERSITY

"Imagine you've been pulled over by a police officer," says Steven Pinker, Harvard psychologist, prolific author, and one of Britannica's *100 Most Influential Scientists of All Time*. In this case, you'd like to know if the relationship is adversarial or conspiratorial: In other words, you'd like to know if you can bribe the cop. But you can't just come out and say it. "Instead, you start by talking about the weather," says Pinker, "and then you mention that it must be difficult to get by on an officer's salary." You start with extremely indirect speech and with every step become slightly more direct. "And after each step, the police officer has the opportunity to accept or rebuff the overture," says Pinker. If the police officer isn't open to being bribed, he or she should cut you off at the weather, before you've incriminated yourself.

Pinker explains this in terms of game theory, with payoffs shown here:

	Dishonest Cop	Honest Cop
NO Bribe	Ticket	Ticket
Yes Bribe	Free	Arrest
Indirect Bribe	Free	Ticket

It's like trying to sleep with a coworker.

"The mistake of Clarence Thomas was to jump steps in this continuum," says Pinker. Thomas brought up the subject of porn videos when he should've prepped that level of directness, perhaps by "asking Anita Hill to call him by his first name, or by adopting a less formal style of speech." Thomas went straight to the equivalent of handing the cop a fifty-dollar bill, dooming himself to a scandal and the closest Senate confirmation in a century.

So language must match the relationship. "This is what we call 'tact,'" says Pinker. And when it doesn't, it creates uncomfortable friction—it's what drives the awkward comedy in a sketch posted to YouTube in which Irish comedian Dave Allen uses the terms "buddy," "chum," "friend," and "mate" with strangers and thus comes off as tactlessly aggressive. This would be like me trying to speak Cockney rhyming slang in a London pub, or walking into a group of local surfers and saying, "Yo brahs—where you shreddin' the swell today?" Language that oversteps the bounds of a relationship is in every way the equivalent of trying to hold hands with a stranger on the subway.

But what's even cooler is this: "Not only does language reflect a relationship, but it can serve to create or change it," says Pinker. And so if you can avoid overstepping in your slow evolution of indirect to direct language with a police officer or attractive coworker, not only can you discover the nature of the relationship, but you can pull the relationship along with it.

So make a script. Start with nearly innocuous comments that are almost certain to be taken as such ("It was nice to see you in the meeting today"). Then move ever so slowly toward the midground ("Wow, that's a sexy haircut!"). Then move glacially toward the thinly veiled overture you're trying to make (Pinker writes, "Would you like to come over sometime and see my etchings?"). Done tactfully and without overstepping, this language of closeness can create closeness.

Note that this entry doesn't necessarily recommend bribing cops or sleeping with coworkers, mirroring a common ethical dilemma in science: just because you can doesn't mean you should.

EAT FOR EIGHT HOURS, LOSE WEIGHT

Satchidananda Panda REGULATORY BIOLOGY, SALK INSTITUTE

"If you overlay the CDC diabetes map with the NASA nighttime satellite map, there's an almost perfect match," says Satchin Panda, regulatory biology specialist at the Salk Institute. The more light in a region at night, the higher the incidence of diabetes. According to Panda, this is because your liver needs sleep. Actually, it's not the sleep per se that your liver needs, but a defined period of fasting each day, which throughout humanity's evolutionary history was the hours of darkness when you couldn't really do much but snooze.

"We started out as diurnal," says Panda, "but learning to control fire allowed us to get away from diurnal needs and into nocturnal space." All of a sudden, we could spend all day hunting and still

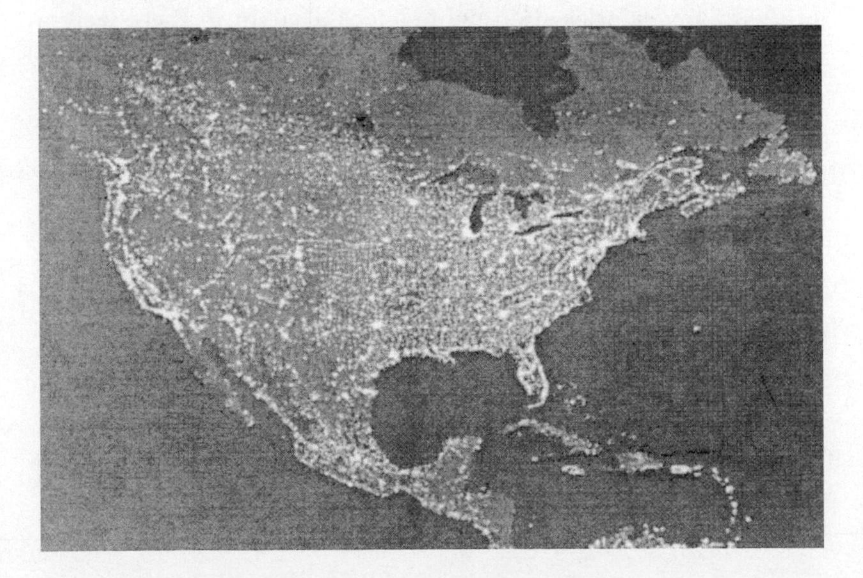

cook and eat the catch once the sun went down. Then with electricity and the industrial revolution, we went a step further—why make widgets during only twelve hours of daylight when you can flip on the lights and run the assembly line for twenty-four hours a day? Thus was shift work born.

"People who work at night have a 150 percent higher rate of metabolic disease," says Panda. And with people in the United States now averaging more than 160 hours of TV viewing per month, "we have 100 to 120 million people who are social shift workers," says Panda. Did you think the twinkling lights on the NASA nighttime map that align so evenly with the diabetes map were due to factory lights? Nope. They're due in large part to the throbbing screens that stay on in American households long after dark. Led by the TV's silver tongue, Americans have made the social decision to act like shift workers. "And this population is more at risk for every type of metabolic disease," says Panda.

The first reason for this is obvious: If you're awake more, you eat more. Panda points out that Americans consume 30 percent of their daily calories after eight o'clock at night. If there were a way to create a nighttime auditory map, you'd hear the roar of a great, collective munching in those same regions you see the light of TV screens.

But the effects of this nighttime munching go a step further than simply packing on extra pounds.

Let's take a closer look at your liver. Among its many functions is storing excess calories as glycogen and then, when you're starving, converting this glycogen into usable glucose. Actually, it's the liver's little autonomous mitochondria that do this, and like any population of millions of single-celled organisms, they're constantly dying and dividing, which in the case of your liver generally maintains a constant population. And, generally, it's at night, when their food processing duties are (or should be) decreased, that these mitochondria do their dividing.

"Our circadian clock separates functions throughout the day so that our organs stay healthy," says Panda. Mitochondria don't multitask well—if they work when they're dividing, they're much more prone to making faulty copies of their DNA. Over time, mutations creep in, and down that path lies all sorts of metabolic badness.

And the clock in your liver isn't a sundial—it doesn't simply monitor lightness and darkness and click through its organ functions based on time of day. Instead, "it gets information about time by when we eat," says Panda. Your liver needs to know when you've taken your last bite of the evening so that it can tell mitochondria it's safe to divide. "And if you eat all the time, the clock gets the clue too many times, it tries to adjust too many times, and it never knows when it's breakfast," says Panda.

Many millions of years precede electricity, and it's this great chunk of time for which our bodies are optimized. Simply, evolution hasn't had enough time to prepare us for nighttime work—our clock isn't nearly nimble enough to flip its schedule to allow efficient night sleeping on the weekend, following day sleeping during the workweek (and instantly back again).

Panda explored this with mice. Mice who are given the ability to eat for only eight hours a day quickly adjust their habits to consume the same number of calories as mice that are allowed to eat for sixteen hours per day. So given an equal calorie count, you might not expect any health differences between eight-hour and sixteen-hour feeding mice. But eight-hour mice live longer. And everyone knows that mice given a high-fat diet gain weight, right? But Panda's new work shows they don't—not if they consume this high-fat diet in an eight-hour window.

"Look at one-hundred-year-olds around the world, across all

different diets, and across all different professions, and you find one common denominator," says Panda. "They always stick to a scheduled feeding pattern, and they always have an early dinner followed by a defined fasting time."

So if you want to live long and prosper, don't eat at night. If you want to lose weight on your current high-fat diet, eat your calories in an eight-hour window.

What's the basis of our biological clock?
Panda found that it's cells in our eyes that express the photopigment melanopsin, which allows us to measure the intensity of ambient light. The more light, the more melanopsin is expressed, and the more awake our biological clock allows us to feel. An older person who has difficulty falling asleep at night may have perfect sight, but blindness to light intensity due to faulty production of melanopsin. Likewise, if you're wide awake after a flight from Los Angeles to New York, you soon might be able to take a pill that shuts down melanopsin, allowing you to sleep when you get in.

A Swedish study of identical twins separated at birth found that lifestyle trumps genetics in determining how long people live. Writing about the study in the *New York Times*, Jane Brody describes the secrets of a long life as "the Three 'R's' of resolution, resourcefulness, and resilience." Extroversion, optimism, self-esteem, and strong ties to community help too.

HOW TO BUILD TINY, FLYING CYBORG BEETLES

Michel Maharbiz ELECTRICAL ENGINEERING, UNIVERSITY OF CALIFORNIA-BERKELEY

"Humans can't build tiny things that fly autonomously," says Michel Maharbiz, electrical engineering and computer science guru at Berkeley. "As you scale things down a couple problems come up." One is airflow: "Turbulence and optimal wing structure are different for a tiny flier than they are for an airplane. Small things fly more like a two-armed chopper, horizontally sweeping," says Maharbiz, who's extremely entertaining to chat with because he says things like "Mike Dickinson at Caltech is one smart mo-fo!" or "My entertainment in life is to build cool shit."

And then there's the power problem. "You can't miniaturize the combustion engine enough," says Maharbiz, "and lithium-ion batteries are ten to forty times less efficient than burning hydrocarbons." To power a tiny flier, the power provided has to be worth the engine weight. Currently, it's not.

Finally, we can't build the actuator part of it, "the little muscles and skeletal components," says Maharbiz. Again, at least not efficiently enough for its power to justify its weight.

So there you go. The answer to, Can we build tiny, flying spybots? is No, not yet.

But nature can.

"There's tons of these things flying around," says Maharbiz. "They eat for energy, and they're great at miniaturizing flight systems."

We call them bugs. And while we can't build tiny flying robots, we're getting better at collaborating with nature on tiny flying cyborgs.

Cyborg green June beetles, to be precise. (Which, as you'll note, is pretty frickin' sweet.) Guys like Maharbiz favor these beetles because the bugs are big enough to carry some gadgetry and small enough to do things like deploy as a swarm into a collapsed building to search for the biosignatures of survivors, or fly through combat areas gathering information without being blasted.

Here's how it works.

First, Maharbiz implants a thin silver wire just behind the beetle's eye into the flight control center of its brain. To it, he attaches a tiny battery repurposed from a cochlear implant. An electric pulse of about -1.5 V starts the beetle's wings, and the same positive pulse stops them. (One can only imagine that a stronger pulse would transform a beetle into a firefly.)

Then the trick is steering.

"You can either pack a muscle full of force fibers or tubes that suck up energy," says Maharbiz, "so muscles can either be strong or fast, not both." So to get the (fast) rate of wing strokes at the (strong) power needed to fly, evolution's equipped beetles with a sweet little oscillator that allows them to pump their wing muscles once—hard!—and count on rebounding musculature to keep the wings pumping for another four beats. It's like the rebound of a stick off a drumhead—one stroke for five beats, repeat as necessary for flight and/or the opening of the iconic 20th Century Fox fanfare.

What this means is that a beetle's wings can only buzz at one speed—the oscillator rebounds at a fixed rate, so you can't simply drive beetle wings faster or slower for increased or decreased thrust. Still, Maharbiz found that wires delivering pulses to these resonators could control the amplitude of wing beats. Both wires pulsing 10 Hz at ten beats per second for three seconds increases wing amplitude and makes the beetle gain altitude. The same pulse in only the right wing makes the beetle turn left—like paddling harder with the right oar of a rowboat. By uniformly throttling down the wing amplitude, you can land the beetle.

The cool part is that precision piloting isn't needed here. "We don't try to fly the beetle—we try to *guide* the beetle," says

Maharbiz. Nature remains the pilot, used for leveling to the horizon, powering the system, and all the other intricacies of flight currently lost to human engineers.

A quick online search returns video of the cyborg beetle in action as well as a pdf with the full specs for creating your own. Seriously.

Maharbiz writes, "When I dream of the future, I see machines built from what we would now call 'living things': tables that are derived from plant cell lines, which breathe your office air and use ambient light for energy to fix themselves or grow new parts; houses whose walls are alive and whose infrastructure hosts an ecology of organisms who perform tasks both microscopic and macroscopic; computational elements whose interfaces completely blur the line between cell and chip."

HOW TO LEARN

Robert Bjork PSYCHOLOGY, UNIVERSITY OF CALIFORNIA–LOS ANGELES

The one hundred-ish skills in this book can help make you awesome. But your ability to put them to use is bound by one thing: your ability to learn. The more you can learn, the more awesome you can become. So consider this a keystone entry.

First, think about how you attack a pile of study material. "People tend to try to learn in blocks," says Robert Bjork, Distinguished Professor of Psychology at UCLA, "mastering one thing before moving on to the next." But instead he recommends interleaving, a strategy in which, for example, instead of spending an hour working on your tennis serve, you mix in a range of skills like backhands, volleys, overhead smashes, and footwork. "This creates a sense of difficulty," says Bjork, "and people tend not to notice the immediate effects of learning." Instead of making an appreciable leap forward with your serving ability after a session of focused practice, interleaving forces you to make nearly imperceptible steps forward with many skills. But over time, the sum of these small steps is much greater than the sum of the leaps you would have taken if you'd spent the same amount of time mastering each skill in its turn.

Bjork explains that successful interleaving allows you to "seat" each skill among the others: "If information is studied so that it can be interpreted in relation to other things in memory, learning is much more powerful," he says.

There's one caveat: Make sure the miniskills you interleave are related in some higher-order way. If you're trying to learn tennis, you'd want to interleave serves, backhands, volleys, smashes, and footwork—not serves, synchronized swimming, European capitals, and programming in Java.

Similarly, studying in only one location is great as long as you'll only be required to recall the information in the same location. If you want information to be accessible outside your dorm room, or office, or nook on the second floor of the library, Bjork recommends varying your study location.

And again, these tips generalize. Interleaving and varying your study location will help whether you're mastering math skills, learning French, or trying to become a better ballroom dancer.

So too will a somewhat related phenomenon, the spacing effect, first described by Hermann Ebbinghaus in 1885. "If you study and then you wait, tests show that the longer you wait, the more you will have forgotten," says Bjork. That's obvious—over time, you forget. But here's the cool part: If you study, wait, and then study again, the longer the wait, the more you'll have learned after this second study session. Bjork explains it this way: "When we access things from our memory, we do more than reveal it's there. It's not like a playback. What we retrieve becomes more retrievable in the future. Provided the retrieval succeeds, the more difficult and involved the retrieval, the more beneficial it is." Note that there's a trick implied by "provided the retrieval succeeds": You should space your study sessions so that the information you learned in the first session remains just barely retrievable. Then, the more you have to work to pull it from the soup of your mind, the more this second study session will reinforce your learning. If you study again too soon, it's too easy.

Along these lines, Bjork also recommends taking notes just after class, rather than during—forcing yourself to recall a lecture's information is more effective than simply copying it from a blackboard. "Get out of court stenographer mode," says Bjork. You have to work for it. The more you work, the more you learn, and the more you learn, the more awesome you can become.

"Forget about forgetting," says Robert Bjork. "People tend to think that learning is building up something in your memory and that forgetting is losing the things you built. But in some respects the opposite is true." See, once you learn something, you never actually forget it. Do you remember your childhood best friend's phone number? No? Well, Dr. Bjork showed that if you were reminded, you would retain it much more quickly and strongly than if you were asked to memorize a fresh seven-digit number. So this old phone number is not forgotten—it lives somewhere in you—only, recall can be a bit tricky.

And while we count forgetting as the sworn enemy of learning, in some ways that's wrong too. Bjork showed that the two live in a kind of symbiosis in which forgetting actually aids recall. "Because humans have unlimited storage capacity, having total recall would be a mess," says Bjork. "Imagine you remembered all the phone numbers of all the houses you had ever lived in. When someone asks you your current phone number, you would have to sort it from this long list." Instead, we forget the old phone numbers, or at least bury them far beneath the ease of recall we give to our current number. What you thought were sworn enemies are more like distant collaborators.

Forget just learning. University of California-Davis psychologist Dean Keith Simonton knows how you can become a genius. First, pick the definition of "genius" you're aiming for—superior IQ, prodigious talent, or exceptional achievement. OK, let's be realistic: You've either got Marilyn vos Savant's 228 IQ or you don't, and if you had prodigious talent, you'd already know it.

But the "genius at" category can be trained. Anyone can be Michelangelo at something. "Sometimes it just takes more than the usual amount of time to find your thing," says Simonton. If you haven't got it yet, keep searching. Once you find it—be it topiary, competitive Rubik's cube-ing, folding proteins, or painting creation scenes on inverted domes—"it takes about a decade of hard work to develop domain-specific skills," says Simonton.

Get aggressive in your far-and-wide search for your talent. Then retreat to that cave high in the Himalayas, where you can spend ten years perfecting it. When you emerge—BAM!—you'll be a genius.

THE BODY LANGUAGE OF DOMINANCE AND LOVE

David Givens ANTHROPOLOGY, CENTER FOR NONVERBAL STUDIES

Who hasn't needed to bluff? In business, sports, and romantic pursuit, it's often useful to seem more powerful—or more vulnerable—than you really are. Sure, you can try flashing a smile or a frown or a come-hither, but "we've learned to control our faces," says David Givens, director of the Center for Nonverbal Studies, in Spokane, Washington. And so people have learned to be wary of them. If you want to bluff convincingly—and figure out what others are really thinking—you'll need to focus on another body part.

"Our shoulders are much less tutored," says Givens.

For instance, the shrug is reflexive, and because it's unfiltered by the scheming brain, it's telling.

This is because the shrug comes from your inner lizard. And this lizard part of the brain knows how to show subordination—it crouches. Specifically, lizards duck their heads while rotating their lower arms outward, thus lowering their bodies. Mammals do it too—witness my yellow Lab in the second after I've caught him neck-deep in the Thanksgiving turkey. We call this cowering. In humans, it's the knee-jerk response to "Look out!" and also the who knows? gesture that shows subservience and uncertainty in classrooms and boardrooms around the world.

Opposite the cringe is what Givens calls "the antigravity sign." This is humans' palm-down speaking gesture or the high-stand display of a dominant lizard. "People in the military or business try to mimic this gesture by augmenting the shoulders and squaring them with uniforms and suits," says Givens. Again, witness my yellow Lab, whose shoulder hackles flare threateningly when he's confronted with intense danger in the form of squirrels on the porch or (for some reason) pumpkins. Make your shoulders bigger, and you'll look badder.

And once you're done being big and bad, perhaps you'll take a second to reconnect with your softer side. Just as there are evolutionarily programmed signals for dominance and subservience, there are hardwired signals of love (admit it—these signals are why you're still reading this entry). You know about the neck-revealing hair adjustment and the one-eyebrow-raised smoldering smile. But did you know about pigeon toes? Givens points to it as a sure sign of attraction. Toes in means "come hither" and toes out—reminiscent of a soldier at rest—means "not today, maybe not ever." Also on a spectrum from inviting to denying is head angle: Forehead down, eyes up should make you recall Lauren Bacall's famous come-hither to Humphrey Bogart. And on the flip side, chin up with eyes looking down is bad, bad news—a sure sign of disdain.

If you're seeing pigeon toes and downward forehead along with the vulnerable lizard shrug, your evening is looking up. All together, you know what it looks like? Well, it looks exactly like Betty Boop. That naughty minx.

Givens is quick to point out that not only can you learn to recognize these signs in their natural habitat and thus know things you might otherwise not, but you can learn to control them for your own evil purposes (my words, not his). These collected signals not only function as subconscious conduits of information, but they can create reciprocity, too.

You want a better chance with that special someone you glimpsed across the bar? Get your pigeon-toed, forehead-tilting, shoulder-shrugging groove on. You might want to practice in the mirror first.

David Givens's books include *Love Signals*
and *Your Body at Work*. His nonverbal dictionary is online at www.center-for-nonverbal-studies.org.

Body language isn't solely the domain of the living. Cynthia Breazeal of MIT's Media Lab creates robots that rock nonverbal communication. "We've seen that if doctor-patient or teacher-student nonverbal behavior is compatible, health and learning outcomes are improved," says Breazeal, and she's seen the same with her 'bots—her robots that guide users' weight loss or education are most successful when their choices to remind, persuade, cajole, or bully their humans gels with users' personalities. Going a step further, she says, "We're experimenting with robots that have a version of mirror neurons," referring to the cells in the human brain that allow us to internally imitate others' behavior, thus inferring their feelings and intentions. Similarly, Breazeal's robots now learn to imitate the gestures and interaction patterns of their users, making themselves both more liked and more persuasive.

HOW AND WHEN TO OVERRULE CHOICE

Sheena Iyengar SOCIAL PSYCHOLOGY, COLUMBIA BUSINESS SCHOOL

In American culture, "Choice is more than a decision," says Sheena Iyengar, social psychologist at the Columbia Business School. The desire for choice is so strong in our culture that the word's become an adjective describing something good—as in a choice chicken breast.

"At the most basic level, we're born with the desire for choice," says Iyengar. "But we're not born knowing how to make a choice." Instead, culture teaches us how to choose.

To make a broad comparison, American culture teaches people to make choices as individuals, whereas Asian cultures teach people to make choices in consultation with a group. "We can decide what we're going to be, whom we're going to marry, what we're going to eat. But if you go to Japan, what you're going to wear or whom you're going to marry is seen as such an important choice that it's made in consultation with important others," says Iyengar.

In a TED talk (www.Ted.com), Iyengar illustrates this point with the following story. In Japan, Iyengar ordered green tea with sugar. No, the waiter informed her, one does not take sugar with green tea. Iyengar persisted in her desire for sweetened tea and eventually pushed her request up the food chain (as it were) to the restaurant's manager, who informed her that, unfortunately, the kitchen was out of sugar. In that case, Iyengar asked for a cup of coffee instead. The coffee arrived on a saucer with a small pitcher of cream . . . and two packets of sugar.

In this case and in this culture, the decision to embarrass herself with the improper addition of sugar to tea was not Iyengar's alone—it was the group's responsibility to ensure she made what was so certainly (unbeknownst to Iyengar) the best choice.

This was one of the original roles of religion, says Iyengar—to help us inform our decisions with input from our significant prefrontal cortexes, rather than depending on some willy-nilly demand for sugar from our id. In order to conquer this classic self-control problem, we gave God the right to make our choices for us about killing, coveting, watching football on Sunday, and how we prepare and eat many of our foods.

The problem is that we American neo-heathens have the tendency to let our ids run wild, unbound by the wise words of elders or the dictates of proscriptive religion. For example, Iyengar was *this close* to taking sugar in her green tea, and certainly would have if it weren't for the swift and decisive intervention of the restaurant staff. That's a trivial example, but the implications are real. All by your lonesome, without similar wise oversight or religious dictates, how can you be assured of doing the right thing?

One way is to make your own commandments. "We can make

our own rules—look at Confucius," says Iyengar. These may include "I will not have cake in the house," or "If I fail to exercise three times in the course of a week, I will donate twenty dollars to the most egregious cause I can find," or "I will not date my friends' exes, no matter how attractive and charming they may seem." These rules can overrule choice and used enough, they become habit.

This reminds me of eminent physicist and jokester Richard Feynman, who wrote in his autobiography (which remains one of my all-time favorite books) about his decision while studying at MIT to always, from that point forward, eat chocolate ice cream for dessert. In his opinion, this rule eliminated an unwanted nightly choice—what to have for dessert—and left him free to focus on more important matters, like how to pick locks and convince his colleagues that he spoke every possible language.

So ask yourself, Does a choice lead to beneficial/delectable variety, or does it include a clear winner in competition with attractive but detrimental alternatives? If it's the first, keep the choice as a choice. But if it's the second, delegate/relegate it to your rulebook. In a world in which choice knows no cultural or religious bounds, the best rules to live by may be your own.

Iyengar explored the proverb "Success is getting what you want, but happiness is wanting what you get," with college seniors entering the job market. Seniors who were maximizers completed exhaustive searches and took jobs paying on average 20 percent more than satisficers, who spent much less time searching and took lower-paying jobs. But satisficers were measurably more satisfied with the jobs they landed—perhaps because maximizers relied more on external than internal measures of success in job seeking, and were more aware of the opportunities that didn't pan out.

THE COOLEST CARD TRICK EVER

Ian Stewart MATHEMATICS, UNIVERSITY OF WARWICK

Ian Stewart, mathematician, prolific puzzle author, and very fun person to chat math with, explains the following best card trick I've ever seen, invented by mathemagician Art Benjamin at Harvey Mudd College.

First, prepare a stack of sixteen cards so that cards 1, 6, 11, and 16 are the four aces. Now deal them facedown in four rows of four. Turn up cards 3, 8, 9, and 14 to make the arrangement shown on page 20.

OK, you're done with the setup and ready to start the trick proper. Ask your dupe to imagine the grid as a sheet of paper and to "fold" it along any straight horizontal or vertical line between cards (as shown on page 21).

Continue "folding" along any lines until you've restacked the cards into one pack of sixteeen. Done right, twelve cards should be facedown and four should be faceup (or vice versa). Of course, the trick seems destined to return the original four faceup cards. And that would be neat. But what's even neater is that no matter

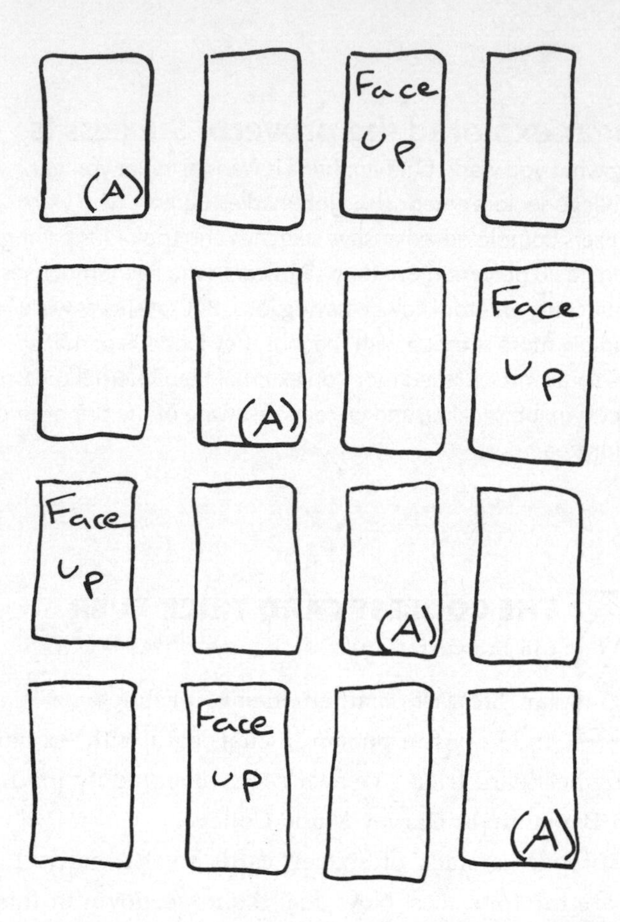

how you fold the grid of sixteen, the four cards that face opposite the others are—wait for it . . . wait for it—the FOUR ACES!

I had to do this trick three times to believe that it actually works. (It does.) Alternatively, I could have listened more closely to Stewart's explanation.

"The number two is very important," he says. Odd and even is a fundamental property of mathematics, and in this trick means that if you flip a card an even number of times, it ends with its original up side facing up. If you flip it an odd number of times, the side that was down faces up. Now imagine arranging this trick's sixteen cards in the pattern of a chessboard, as shown on page 22.

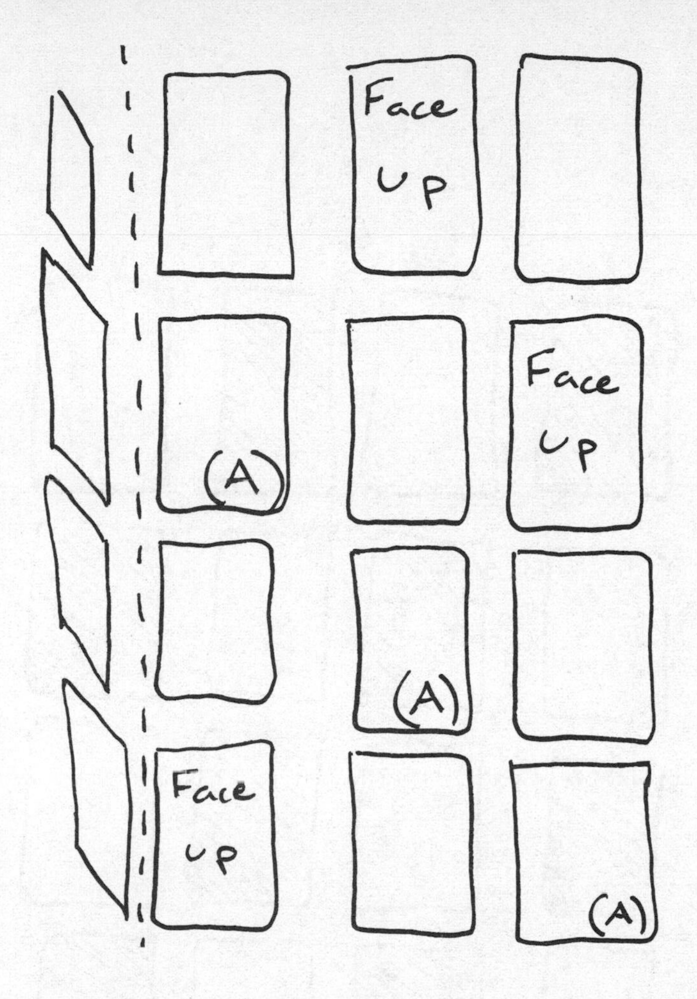

However you fold a chessboard, all the white spaces undergo exactly one more or one fewer flip than the black spaces—one is odd and one is even—and so no matter how you fold chessboard-patterned cards, they will eventually turn into a pile of sixteen cards all facing the same way. Try it. But in this trick, you didn't arrange the cards like a chessboard, did you? No. Exactly four cards in this trick's setup differ from the chessboard pattern. And so these same four cards will point the wrong way in your folded stack.

Of course, these cards are the four aces.

Ian Stewart studies animal gaits and knows why a cat always lands on its feet. It's a surprisingly interesting question: A nonrotating, upside-down cat that becomes a nonrotating right-side-up cat seems to break the laws of mechanics. Where does this phantom rotation come from?

"Our first cat couldn't do it," says Stewart, "and my wife tried to train him by holding him upside down above a cushion." Presumably this was for the cat's safety and not purely for entertainment. (Yes, after reviewing a draft of this entry, Stewart confirmed safety was indeed the motive.) What cats other than Stewart's rotationally challenged feline do is use the physics of merry-go-rounds. They twist their back legs in one direction and counterbalance by twisting their front legs in the other direction. Great: equal and opposite.

But here's the trick: The cat pulls in its front legs and extends its back legs, so that its front undergoes more rotation (just like the body-in/body-out speed trick of merry-go-rounds . . . that is, before they were banned from American playgrounds for reasons of safety and pediatric wussification). Then the cat repeats and reverses the operation, extending its front legs, which act as a rotational anchor allowing the constricted back legs to catch up.

Voilà! Without turning Newton in his grave, the cat has turned itself butter-side up! It's a neat trick; you can see it happening in slow motion at *National Geographic*'s website by video searching "cat's nine lives."

Puzzle #1: Math Is Too Sexy

As you know, math is extremely stylish. Use well-known physics equations to transform "mat = hematic" into "G = uccci."

HOW TO BET SPORTS

Wayne Winston DECISION SCIENCE, INDIANA UNIVERSITY-BLOOMINGTON

Betting seems like you versus the odds, but in fact it's a mano a mano competition between you and a bookie. And unfortunately, the game's rigged: The standard bookie payout is 10/11, meaning that a win pays ten dollars but you pay eleven dollars for a loss. So bookies don't gamble: They set a statistically fair line so that (theoretically) half the money is bet one way and half the money is bet the other. Each loser pays for a winner, and the bookie cleans up on transaction fees.

It's exactly like roulette: Over time, the losers pay the winners and the 2/34 times the ball lands on green, the casino gets paid.

OK, sports betting isn't exactly like roulette. In sports betting, humans set the opening line. For example, bookies predicted the Lakers and Celtics would score a combined 187 total points in Game 7 of the 2010 NBA Finals. You could've bet over or under this total. Or bookies had the Colts winning by 5 points over the Saints in the 2010 Super Bowl. You could've taken Colts -5 or Saints +5.

With the bookies' rake (much different than the sports fundraiser rookies' bake), you have to beat the line more than 52.4 percent of the time to make money. And it comes down to this: Who's got the best kung fu, you or the Wookiees—er . . . bookies?

Wayne Winston, decision science professor at Indiana University, Mark Cuban's former stats guru for the Dallas Mavericks, and author of the book *Mathletics* has especially strong kung fu. (His website, www.WayneWinston.com, is a cornucopia of statistical awesomeness for all things sports.)

One of his nicer attempts at a Shaolin throw down was trying to beat the NBA over/under by including referees' influence on total score. Basically, a ref who calls more fouls creates a higher final score—free throws are easy points and players in foul trouble can't defend as aggressively. This is what former NBA referee (and convicted felon) Tim Donaghy did—he called more fouls or allowed teams to play in order to manipulate the total points scored. But other referees are naturally permissive or restrictive. For example, from 2003 to 2008, when the referee Jim Clark officiated, teams went over the predicted total 221 times and under the predicted total 155 times (more ref data at Covers .com). Bingo! It looks like you can make money! Just bet the over whenever Jim Clark's on the ticket!

But it's not that easy. First, there are three refs on any NBA ticket. Averaging their predicted over/under makes any single ref less powerfully predictive. And you're also counting on the idea that past performance is going to equal future prediction. This is a problem with most mathematical modeling: You look into the past and hope like heck the future's going to be similar. But what if Jim Clark realized he'd been calling games too tight and decided to ref a little differently this year? You'd be out of luck.

As was Wayne Winston, who found refs could help him beat the NBA total over/under more than 50 percent of the time, but not more than the 52.4 percent he needed in order to make money. Unfortunately, he says, bookies in the big three sports—football, baseball, and basketball—are very sophisticated and tend to set very good opening lines—you're as likely to win on one side of the line as you are on the other.

But what happens after a bookie sets a line? Well, it moves based on how people bet. If a basketball over/under started at 187 points and for whatever reason more people bet over, the line might jump to 190 points to encourage equal money on either side. Remember, bookies don't want risk and to avoid it, the over has to match the under.

So when an opening line is released into the wild, it goes from being a statistical system to being a human system. And human systems are beholden to irrationality. For example, take Roger Federer versus Rafael Nadal. You'd have a tough time beating the line in Vegas, but what about in Zurich or in Madrid? People like to bet their home team, and so after a statistically accurate opening line hits the streets in Switzerland, Swiss bookies are likely to see more money bet on Federer. To avoid risk, the line would adjust to encourage bets on Nadal. If Vegas thought Federer/Nadal was an even match, a bet might pay 1:1, but a bookie in Geneva might give people 1:1.2 odds to encourage the otherwise-inclined Swiss to bet Nadal.

When you find inequalities between bookies, what's the best thing to do? Well, one option is arbitrage: You can bet both. Imagine putting $100 on Federer with a Spanish bookie paying 1:1.2, and $100 on Nadal with a Swiss bookie paying 1.2:1. No matter who wins, you lose $100 and win $120. But, Winston points out, differences in bookies are likely to be very small and so only big-money bets earn anything appreciable in arbitrage. And throwing big money at a Swiss bookie might change the line. For example, $100,000 on Nadal in Geneva might balance all the hometown fans betting Federer, swinging the payout back to 1:1. And arbitrage websites are likely to rake a little more than the standard 10/11 of Vegas bookies. That said, it's worth keeping your eyes on rivalries, says Winston. "It's probably a crime to bet Serbia in the World Cup if you're living in Croatia."

Here's another tip that Winston recommends (via an article by the economist Steven Levitt): People like to bet NFL favorites. Bookies discovered this, and if the point spread in a certain game should statistically have been +9, bookies found they could set the line at +10 and people would still bet the favorite. Adjusting the line created slightly more losing bets and thus slightly more money for the bookies. Combine this with a hometown favorite and you have a powerful engine of irrationality—emotion leads fans to overbet hometown favorites, and so you can sometimes find unreasonably good odds if you're willing to bet the opposite: Go for visiting-team underdogs, which are statistically likely to cover the inflated point spread.

But if you're looking for consistent money in sports betting, there's one easy rule: Stay away from data. "Where there's not good information, there's inefficiency. And where there's inefficiency, there's money to be made," says Winston. Like the stock market, there are enough people running enough numbers and placing enough bets on football, basketball, and baseball that it's extremely difficult to find something that no one's thought of. Unless you can find and act on information no one else has (insider trading), you're unlikely to beat the opening line 52.4 percent of the time in the big three sports. (Try cricket, says Winston, because the information and the people evaluating it aren't yet supersaturated.)

Puzzle #2: Dr. Stat Cricket Prop

Dr. Stat (as in, "Get me 1,000 cc of espresso, stat!") specializes in betting on a specific cricket bowler. Bookies know that each time the bowler throws, he has a 1/46 chance of knocking the wickets. So betting that any single throw takes a wicket pays forty-six times your wager for a win (for simplicity's sake we'll assume no bookies' rake). What makes this a special prop is the fact that Dr. Stat (and only Dr. Stat) knows this bowler is a cold-weather specialist. When it's below 15°C this bowler adds 1 percent to every throw's chance of taking the wicket. And so Dr. Stat follows this bowler and follows the weather and bets accordingly. If he lays $1,000 per wager over one hundred cold-weather bets, how much money should he expect to win?

The Chevalier de Méré was a seventeenth-century French writer who liked to gamble. Or was he a seventeenth-century French gambler who liked to write? Either way, dupes caught on that de Méré's meat-and-potatoes bet—that he could roll any prenamed number in four tries with a six-sided dice—was stacked against them. And so de Méré went a step further, betting he could roll boxcars (double sixes) in twenty-four tries with two dice. That makes sense: The first seems like 4-in-6 odds and the second seems the same only dressed up to look trickier at 24-in-36 odds.

Only it's not nearly that simple. Over time the bet just didn't seem to pay off. But why? In his book *What's Luck Got to Do with It*, Marlboro College mathematician Joseph Mazur explains the odds. Let's look at the first bet, first.

Rolling one six-sided die four times yields 6^4, or 1,296, possible patterns—you could roll 2, 2, 2, 2 or 3, 5, 4, 6 or 1, 5, 6, 2 etc. through all 1,296 possible combinations. But in 5^4 of these, you lose—these are all the ones without the number you want—625 ways to lose in all. But check this out: This means there are 1,296 − 625 = 671 ways you can win! Trying to roll a specific number with a six-sided die thrown four times, you win more than you lose, and so it's a good bet for the roller. In fact, the bet has a 671 ÷ 1,296 = 0.52 probability of paying off.

Now let's look at de Méré's second bet: boxcars in twenty-four tries. There are thirty-six different combinations you can get by rolling two six-sided dice. So if you roll these two dice twenty-four times, you can come up with 36^{24} possible combinations; 35^{24} of these combinations lose. These are really, really big numbers that you most certainly don't want to see printed here, but take Mazur's word for it, there are slightly more ways to lose than to win—there's only a 0.49 probability of winning the bet. As de Méré ascertained by his dwindling bankroll, that's bad.

But just one more throw tips the probability over 0.50. So there's another bet you can win: boxcars in twenty-five, not twenty-four, tries.

If you insist on betting big sports, Winston recommends prop bets. These are the strange, in-the-moment conjectures that have become all the rage in Vegas. At the 2010 Super Bowl, the line was 5.5 on how many times the Who's Pete Townshend would do his windmill move. And the line was 2.5 on how many times CBS would cut to Kim Kardashian in the stands.

In the case of prop bets, bookie kung fu may not be very strong. If you can specialize in a certain kind of prop, you may be able to outmaneuver the underpowered bookie underling setting the line. Maybe you can ferret out information or design a more accurate model that allows you to know a bookie's line is a little high or a little low on something like the number of times a certain lineman will be shown firing snot rockets, or how many players in a given season will be fined for comments posted to Twitter.

Or you can run your own prop.

Find something interesting that you think you've got a good line on (see above). And then prop it with odds that only you know are slightly off. Bet to win. Can you prop bet the office pool?

AVOID CONSUMPTION QUICKSAND

Niro Sivanathan ORGANIZATIONAL BEHAVIOR, LONDON BUSINESS SCHOOL

Luxury is a status symbol. You tote a $37,000 Hermès Birkin handbag or drive a million-dollar McLaren F1 to show that you have the wealth to do so. It's a signal that you belong in society—some would say a signal of genetic quality and mate desirability.

At least that's the popular theory.

Niro Sivanathan, professor of organizational behavior at the London Business School, took the theory into the lab to kick the tires. Specifically, he gathered 150 subjects and made them feel bad about themselves. With self-worth thus threatened, subjects said they'd pay more for luxury cars and watches than did subjects allowed to retain their self-worth. Interestingly, though, devalued people's valuation of ordinary goods—ones that had no relation to status—was unaffected.

In Sivanathan's words, "Subjects with low self-esteem sought to heal ego threat with consumption of status goods." If you feel your inherent worth is lacking, you seek to buy your way back to a full self.

So don't shop when you feel crappy about yourself. You'll overspend.

But that's just the start.

In a follow-up study, Sivanathan measured the natural self-esteem of a cross section of American consumers. Then he had subjects read about and suggest a price for a luxury car. As you might guess, people below the average income of $50,233 had significantly lower self-esteem. And these people said they would pay more for the car. "People of low socioeconomic status naturally experience higher levels of threat to self and can be prone to overconsumption of costly, showy goods," says Sivanathan.

This was especially true when credit was involved, which offers less sense of something of yours being transferred to someone else (see this book's entry with Brian Knutson).

And these are the components of what Sivanathan calls "consumption quicksand." "Low self-esteem leads to more consumption on credit, which leads to debt and lower self-esteem, which leads to more consumption," he says. "It's a dangerous positive feedback loop."

Does this quicksand look familiar? If so, you need to break the loop. And Sivanathan knows how.

In a follow-up study, before presenting devalued subjects the chance to splurge on luxury, he encouraged them to reflect on meaningful things—family, health, well-being. Thus recentered, subjects were less likely to overprice luxury goods.

"One reason people consume is to protect the ego," says Sivanathan. But there are other ways to feel good about yourself, including spending time thinking about what's important to you. So in addition to not shopping when you're down, before you walk through a mall-entrance department store, or before you stroll through a car lot on the hunt for a minivan though tempted by a Porsche, take a minute to reflect on your priorities. You'll shield yourself against the mistaken idea that you can buy the missing chunk of your self-esteem.

Niro Sivanathan also explored corporate promotion tournaments, which are competitions with rules and contestants that are commonly used to fill open executive positions. "Just like Barry Bonds used steroids to hit more home runs, organizational actors sabotage, bribe, and assume high risk to get ahead," says Sivanathan. As on the show *Survivor*, competitors in these tournaments also start by eliminating the weakest links, but switch strategy at the midpoint to eliminate the strongest competition. "In this way companies can ensure they instate the best manipulator as CEO and not the best businessperson," says Sivanathan.

HOW TO HANG TEN

Paul Doherty PHYSICS, THE EXPLORATORIUM

As a former SoCal transplant, I went surfing thrice in three years, all when gung-ho friends visited with the idea of catching a wave, snapping a pic, and posting something to Facebook that would make friends in the rainy Northwest or icy Northeast feel even worse about their environs than they did already. And after each of these three sessions, I was completely flabbergasted by something I may otherwise never have had the opportunity to notice: how much salt water the human sinus cavities can hold. Really, days later I'd be leaning over to tie my shoes and a stream of water would leak from my nose. I imagined that when the same happened to my friends, now back in some office in Seattle or New York, they used the salt water as a welcome conversation starter about the gnarly waves they shredded off the SoCal coast. Does this kind of thing win dates in the lands of rain and snow, or does leakage from one's sinuses remain repulsive no matter what?

Anyway, the roundabout point is that there are many steps before hanging ten. The first is catching a wave. (Actually, the first is finding the right point in the right wave, but that's another long hydrologic story.) It seems easy: The wave pushes, your board moves, and you stand up. But, "catching a wave is actually an amazingly complex computation," says Paul Doherty, who earned a PhD in physics from MIT and taught at Oakland University before founding the Center for Teaching and Learning at San Francisco's Exploratorium. Beginning surfers paddle and kick furiously. Experienced surfers "know the wave and know their bodies, and can match the wave's speed in a couple strokes," says Doherty. If you're too slow, the wave pushes right past you. Too fast and you're out ahead—and when you slow down from fatigue or to let the wave catch up, you're too slow and it blows right past you.

So watch from the shore as sets roll in—how much paddle power do the best surfers need to match the waves' speed? And try chasing a couple waves after they've rolled past to get a feeling for how hard you have to paddle to keep up with them.

Then there's the matter of where to stand on the board—the genesis of most of the salt water in my sinus cavities.

"Every surfboard has a center of buoyancy," explains Doherty.

This is the point where, if the board was floating in the water, you could push down with your fist and the entire board would sink equally. And a surfer has a center of gravity—the point over which your mass pushes directly down. "If the center of gravity is behind the center of buoyancy, the tail of the surfboard sinks and the nose comes up," says Doherty. This causes the board to decelerate and pull back through the wave. The opposite is my nemesis: As a surfer's center of gravity moves ahead of the board's center of buoyancy, the board's nose digs beneath onrushing water, sending the would-be surfer tumbling, and compacting salt water deep, deep into the sinus cavities.

But imagine if you get the speed and the centers of mass/buoyancy right. Finally you're standing! You're really standing! "You're on a strange sliding board riding down an up escalator, which also happens to be moving forward laterally," says Doherty. After sliding straight down the wave's face, if you somehow avoid digging the nose of your board into the trough at the wave's base, your momentum takes you far ahead of the wave . . . at which point you decelerate, start to sink, and are flattened by the wave as it catches you, prone and quivering.

This is why you need to turn across the wave. Turn now. Turn before it's too late. The best surfers seem to catch waves having already started their cut across its face. Intermediate or big-wave surfers make a turn near the wave's base and cut back into it. Beginning surfers become intimate with salt water.

But in addition to staying afloat, there's another neat thing about the turn: It allows you to accelerate to faster than wave speed (if you're into that sort of thing). At the bottom of a turn, you push not only against the force of gravity, but against the centripetal force of the turn itself (see this book's entry describing how to take a corner). If you're crouching down at the bottom of the turn and then stand while turning, the energy of your legs pushes against this centripetal force like a skateboarder on a half-pipe, pumping energy into the system, which, in this case, makes you go faster.

And now, rocketing around the wave in arcs and slashes, you have but one task left: hanging ten, or intentionally shifting your center of gravity as far forward as the board allows in order to hang your toes off its front edge in a move that is just as awesome as it is suicidal. Surely holding this position defies the laws of physics?

Doherty points out that the key to hanging ten is not what happens at the (suicidal) front of the board, but what happens at the back. If a surfer is hanging ten, you can be sure the board's tail is no longer buoyant on the surface of the wave. Instead, it's shoved back into the breaking wave like a pry bar under a heavy object, counterbalancing the weight of the surfer up front. This is one reason hanging ten is a move reserved for longboarders—you need a lengthy pry bar for leverage.

Read. Visualize. Learn. As for me, I moved to Colorado.

A quick search for Paul Doherty finds his Exploratorium homepage, where he describes about 250 very cool hands-on science experiments, including how to make a lava lamp and how to ollie a skateboard.

I would maybe have surfed more if it weren't for a 2010 article in the *Santa Barbara Independent* describing a kayaker in the Channel whose boat was mouthed by a great white shark. But what if my board could protect me from sharks? A surfboard patent application by inventor Guerry Grune describes its included locator device and alarm, alerting the user to "large aquatic animals" as well as a "signal generator configured for transmitting interference signals to disrupt the electrosensory perception system of the aquatic animals." That, truly, is awesome.

HOW TO SELL FOR BIG BUCKS ON EBAY

Gillian Ku ORGANIZATIONAL BEHAVIOR, LONDON BUSINESS SCHOOL

Using an idea imported from Switzerland (where else?), Chicago and New York invited local artists to decorate fiberglass cows. For a set display period, these cows graced city public areas, after which the bovine couture was auctioned, with the proceeds going to charity. Toronto did moose. Boston did cod. St. Paul did Snoopys.

In addition to stuffing cash in city coffers and (presumably) providing mad backyard kitsch for winning bidders, the Cow Parade program created huge amounts of auction data. How do you sell a painted version of a city's iconic animal for the biggest possible bucks? You put bidders in a live setting, ratchet up the time pressure, and create competition. The more emotional arousal you can create in bidders, the higher the eventual selling price. Simply, when people lose their heads, they reach for their wallets.

Gillian Ku, assistant professor of organizational behavior at the

London Business School, wondered if the same would be true on eBay. She got data from (where else?) cows. Specifically, from an eBay seller with the screen name Browncow, who was selling Tommy Bahama shirts. "He was manipulating whether shirts had straightforward descriptions or puffed descriptions," says Ku—you know, descriptions that promise the most amazing shirt ever that hot strangers will want to rip from your body!!!! That's puffery. And it helped sell Tommy Bahama shirts.

But only if a couple other things were true too. One of these factors was starting price. And here's where it starts to get interesting.

Gillian Ku found that eBay starting prices throw conventional economics on its ear. "It should be all about anchoring," she says—meaning that a high starting price should signal an item's worth and lead to a higher selling price. This is what Steve Jobs did when he anchored the price of an iPhone at $599, making the on-sale price of $299 look like a steal. "But what we found on eBay is that low starting prices, not high prices, led to a higher selling price."

But (again), only if a couple other things were true too.

If an auction was misspelled, a higher starting price provided the anchor that economics expects—higher starting price equals higher ending price. And having a reserve price nixed the effect of a low start.

And by this time, Ku started to see a pattern: "It's all about traffic," she says. A low starting price decreases barriers to entry. Having more entrants increases the chances of hooking a serious one. And even bidders who didn't mean to be serious can get sucked into an escalation of commitment by investing time in bidding and rebidding while the price is still low. And finally, high auction traffic in the form of page views and number of bids is another way to signal value—certainly it has high worth because, well, look at all the people who've been here! (It's like evaluating a book's worth based on its number of online reviews—hint, hint.)

Let's be clear: With little traffic, it's best to anchor expectations to a high starting price and list the item in an accurate, businesslike way. If you're going to doom yourself to pitiful traffic by misspelling your item, you'd better hope someone clicks BUY IT NOW. Same if you're listing an item that's so niche, it's inconceivable that many people would give it a look. But if you've got a shot at an auction with more widespread appeal, create traffic with a low starting price, no reserve, and high puffery. This is the competitive arousal model. In cities it created spotted-cow fever, and on eBay it means higher selling prices.

Ku and co found the opposite to be true of negotiations: A high starting price for a firm up for acquisition, salary negotiation, or asking price of a used car leads to a higher final agreement price. The essential difference is the number of possible bidders—in a negotiation, you're only going to have a few buyers, so your best bet is to anchor expectations to a high opening price.

SHOULD YOU MULTITASK?

David Strayer COGNITIVE SCIENCE, UNIVERSITY OF UTAH

I don't multitask. Or, I do it so badly that it quickly devolves into a massive cluster of tangled badness with me standing baffled at its center. This frustrates my wife to no end. She can balance on a beach ball while writing things in her calendar, listening to Radio Lab, text-messaging, and juggling chain saws (it's a neat trick—and also kind of hot). I hold that monotasking allows me to get a string of things done right, one at a time. Kristi thinks that multitasking is a prerequisite for inclusion in post–Stone Age society and that monotaskers should be rounded up and reprogrammed at underground government facilities.

The question is, Should I strive for less inept sessions of multitasking, or should I just give it up completely?

David Strayer, director of the applied cognition lab at the University of Utah, studies multitasking in the fertile realm of distracted driving and found that, "ninety-eight percent of people can't multitask—they don't do either task as well." But here's the interesting part: 2 percent of people can juggle without dropping a ball or, indeed, without any ball even sailing less high—they show no ill effects from multitasking. Strayer calls these people supertaskers. "The question we had," says Strayer, "is, Who are these people?"

To find out, he put supertaskers through a battery of tests, including neuroimaging and genetic evaluation. And he found that, sure enough, the very structure of the supertasker brain looks different than those of 98 percent of us. "These brain regions that differentiate supertaskers from the rest of the population are the same regions that are most different between humans and nonhuman primates," says Strayer. In other words, the brains of supertaskers are just that much further away from those of apes, "the leading edge of evolution," says Strayer. Specifically, "Certain parts of the frontal cortex are recruited in an interesting way," says Strayer. In fact, these areas show less activity when multitasking than do the same areas in normal, human, mammalian, nonalien-overlord brains like mine.

And it's distinct—you either efficiently recruit this region or you don't. You're either a supertasker or you're not. You're either human like me, or a supertasking, blood-drinking, shape-shifting, reptilian alien like my wife.

If you're a supertasker, you know it. Please feel free to continue reading this book while you drive one-handed and one-eyed down the freeway. But if you're not a supertasker, the overwhelming message of science is this: Just give it up already! By multitasking, you do everything less well. Instead, if you want to get the most done right, design your life to monotask. Your brain will thank you for it.

"Writers from Muir to Abbey have talked about the benefits of getting into nature," says Strayer, "but we haven't studied it at a neuroscience level until now."

This is attention restoration theory, based partly on the idea that refraining from multitasking in a text-rich environment might detox, rest, and restore fried neurons in the frontal lobe. While Strayer is quick to say that more research is needed, he points out that from a large pool of anecdotal evidence, "After three days, you start to experience radically different thoughts." (For an example, video search "double rainbow.")

And so there may be hope for me, and by extension all of humanity, yet. If you find your frontal lobe freaking out, head for the hills as quickly as possible. You'll meet me on the way. And if you do, please be alert because I'm likely texting and may swerve dangerously.

Puzzle #3: Multitasking Mix and Match

You have 20 minutes before you need to leave for work, and nine things to accomplish before you go, each of which takes the specified amount of time: brush your teeth (2 min), get dressed (5 min), drink coffee (5 min), make breakfast (5 min), eat breakfast (8 min), check headlines (2 min), read things you were supposed to read for work (5 min), clean (4 min), and fret aimlessly (4 min). Obviously you'll need to multitask. But there are some things that don't go well together—for example, you can't drink coffee or eat breakfast while brushing your teeth. Likewise, you can't eat breakfast until you make it, and can't do either (nor can you brush your teeth) while getting dressed, and aimless fretting can take place only while getting dressed or brushing your teeth. Imagining you can only do a maximum of two things at once, in what order should you complete these six tasks?

TEACH YOUR TODDLER PERFECT PITCH

Diana Deutsch AUDITORY PSYCHOLOGY, UNIVERSITY OF CALIFORNIA–SAN DIEGO

Being a music prodigy would be totally awesome because it would nix the need to converse, cook, flirt, provide, smolder, or otherwise prove your sexiness—you could simply strum your way into your mate's heart.

While studies have shown that becoming a virtuoso is similar to learning a trade—ten years including ten thousand hours of practice seems to do the trick—there's a shortcut to musical maestrosity, allowing you to spend the saved time snogging: Simply be born with perfect pitch, the seemingly innate ability to hear a note and name it. Once you truly hear music, externalizing it through an instrument is as simple as learning to type (mostly . . .).

But if you had perfect pitch, you'd know it, if for no other reason than people whistling in the airport would sound physically, painfully, out of tune. (This according to my friend Ariel, who was an orchestral recorder prodigy before switching to heavy-metal guitar in college and environmental architecture after.) And until recently, experts thought that that was it—at birth, you can hold a note in your mind's ear or you can't. If you're born without the gift, the theory went, your only hope is the consolation prize of painstakingly training relative pitch. For example, learning that the "way up high" leap in "Over the Rainbow" is the interval of a major sixth, as is the iconic leap in the Miles Davis tune "All Blues." Likewise, the first interval in "Twinkle, Twinkle, Little Star" is a perfect fifth. And based on learning these leaps, you can learn to deduce any note on the keyboard given a starting point. In university music programs around the world, a teacher plunks a note, names it, then plunks another note, and students who have successfully trained their relative pitch can name the second note.

But what about naming the first note? What about perfect pitch? What about that shortcut to limitless snogging?

Diana Deutsch, UCSD prof and president of the Society for Music Perception and Cognition, thinks perfect pitch can be trained—but only if you start early.

In part, she bases this opinion on an illusion.

In music, a tritone describes the interval that splits an octave exactly in half. For example, C and F# form the interval of a tritone, and so do the notes D and G#. The interval was banned during the Inquisition as the *diabolus in musica* (the devil in music). Today it starts *The Simpsons* and makes Danny Elfman scores of Tim Burton movies immediately recognizable. Now imagine alternating C and F#, like the siren on a British ambulance. Really, you wouldn't know if the pattern is ascending (C–F#, repeat) or descending (F#–C, repeat).

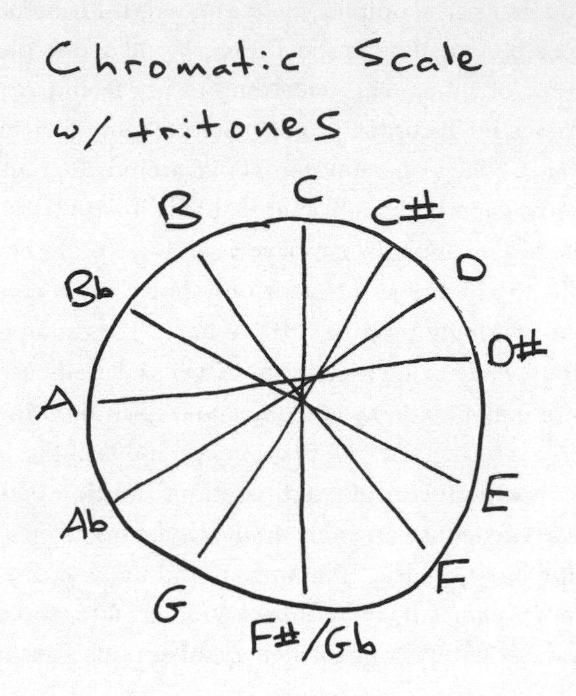

But here's the thing: You do know. Every note has a companion that's exactly half an octave away, and depending on which tritone is played, you perceive the interval as either descending or ascending. And you don't ever switch. It's fixed. Deutsch discovered this tritone paradox and calls it "an implicit form of perfect pitch." Somehow, some way, we all fix notes and hold them in our minds.

So why doesn't the universal ability to hold abstract pitches allow us all to know note names when we hear them? Why—dammit—can't we all be prodigies!

Deutsch found that fixed pitch does, in fact, allow perfect pitch . . . but only in certain cultures.

Sure, an individual American's perception of the tritone paradox is fixed—maybe you hear C–F#–C–F# as an ascending pattern—

but as a culture, Americans may each hear tritones differently. Your friend Barb may hear C–F#–C–F# as a descending pattern. But here's the interesting bit: In Vietnam, the vast majority of the population hears tritone paradoxes in the same way—they're fixed not only on an individual, but on a cultural level.

Blame it on language, says Deutsch. In Vietnamese and other tonal languages, a high "ma" can mean something very different than a low "ma," and so infants learn very early to pair fixed tones with fixed meanings. Later, it's easy to use this same brain mechanism to pair tones with note names like A, B, and C. Deutsch explored data from the Singapore Conservatory and other Asian music schools, and found that—sure enough—the incidence of perfect pitch is much higher in speakers of tonal languages.

Deutsch thinks it might be possible to create a similar mechanism in English speakers. "If your son or daughter has a keyboard at home, use stickers to label the notes with whatever symbols they understand first." If your child recognizes barnyard animals or pictures of family members or colors before he or she recognizes letters, label the keyboard with animal, family, or color stickers. (All G's get a cow, all F's get a pig, etc.) This encourages your budding Beethoven to pair tone with meaning—any meaning works!—which you can then switch to note names once your child knows his or her letters.

It's too late for you—"It seems as if the window for creating this pairing is closed by about age four," says Deutsch—but perhaps early action can allow your progeny to be prodigy.

You can hear examples of the tritone paradox and more cool auditory illusions at Diana Deutsch's faculty homepage: deutsch.ucsd.edu.

You know how to pull a song out of your music library that rocks or soothes. And you know about services like the Internet radio station Pandora or the iTunes "Genius" feature that similarly recommend new music. But what about Zeppelin's "Stairway to Heaven," or other songs that first soothe and then rock, or vice versa, or ping-pong moods from verse to chorus? Drexel University's Youngmoo Kim created an online game, MoodSwings, (music.ece .drexel.edu/mssp) to gather real-time data about songs. As you listen to a song, you move your cursor around quadrants labeled with emotions and for the time your cursor overlaps the areas most chosen by previous users, you rack up points. "Imagine you feel like crap but want to be uplifted," says Kim. With your help, MoodSwings will soon know which songs fit the desired mood trajectory.

HOW TO AGREE (AND WHY NEGOTIATIONS FAIL)

George Loewenstein BEHAVIORAL ECONOMICS, CARNEGIE MELLON UNIVERSITY

Why do people have such a hard time reaching a compromise? Blame fairness.

That's the message of behavioral economist George Loewenstein of Carnegie Mellon University. In many types of negotiations, he says, "People aren't trying to get the maximum payoff, they're just trying to get what they see as fair." And if there's wiggle room in what's fair, parties on opposing sides are likely to wiggle toward opinions of fairness that are personally beneficial, eventually entrenching like four-hundred-pound sumo wrestlers staring each other down across the ring.

Loewenstein offers the following example: Imagine you and I are splitting twenty poker chips. When all's said and done, each chip you're holding will be worth five dollars and each chip I'm holding will be worth twenty dollars (ha!). Now we have to negotiate how to split the twenty chips.

What do you think is fair? Maybe you propose keeping sixteen chips and giving me four. That way, we each get eighty dollars. That's fair.

But wait—the chips are worth more to me than they are to you! What are you going to do with a measly eighty dollars? If I keep all the chips I'll have four hundred dollars. Now that's worth something. Certainly you can see it's better to squeeze the most out of the system, even if you don't happen to be the beneficiary this time, right?

This is an example of a self-serving bias—your idea of fairness is influenced by what's best for you. But there's still hope for agreement. If the top range of my fairness overlaps the bottom range of your fairness, there's shared territory for a deal. But if I'm only willing to give eight chips max, and you're only willing to accept twelve chips min, then we're at loggerheads. In this case, Loewenstein explains, "People are frequently willing to incur a loss rather than take what they see as an unfair payoff."

In other words, we'd rather burn money than share with a cheater. No deal.

To see if self-serving bias jumps the confines of abstract poker chip games, Loewenstein and his colleague Linda Babcock sent letters to all the school board presidents (on one side) and heads of teachers' unions (on the other) in Pennsylvania. The letters asked the boards or unions to make a fair list of the nearby towns that are comparable to their own—like valuing a house, salaries in comparable districts help negotiators set teacher salaries in a target district. Loewenstein and Babcock found that the school board heads consistently listed towns with low teacher salaries, while the heads of teachers' unions consistently listed towns with high teacher salaries.

Which towns were fairly comparable? Well, whichever ones allowed school board presidents to propose lower salaries or union heads to propose higher ones. And generating lists with little overlap was a strong predictor of an eventual strike.

So if you believe you're on the fair side of the fence and I believe I'm on the other fair side of the fence, and between these fences is a gaping demilitarized zone, what's the negotiation solution? "Well," says Loewenstein, "we did a lot of research trying to debias it." How can you remove this pesky self-serving bias? Nix writing an essay about the other side's point of view. It didn't work. Having both sides list the holes in their own case helped a bit.

But check this out: Rather than trying to diffuse self-serving bias, Loewenstein recommends using it to create a solution—the stronger the bias, the better. That's because a strong bias can blind combatants to the idea that a third party could see it any way but their own.

It's not just that I would like at least eight poker chips, but that I believe the abstract idea of fairness is certain to award me at least these eight chips. And you're equally certain you'll get at least the twelve chips at the bottom end of your fairness scale. So we're both happy to let a fair third party make the call, both blithely confident that the outcome will be the one we want. Self-serving bias makes us both likely to agree to arbitration.

When you notice a demilitarized zone between the two fences of entrenched parties, rather than trying to nudge these fences closer together—toward the shared space of agreement—let them stand apart. And pick an arbitrator to split the difference. We're likely to be equally surprised when this impartial third party awards us ten chips each, but you gotta admit it's fair.

George Loewenstein explored the difference between how much people want something and then how much they like it once they get it. With drugs, people almost universally want them more than they end up liking them. With sex, it can be the other way around: People can end up liking sex more than they initially wanted it, especially as both men and women get older, and with more time in a relationship.

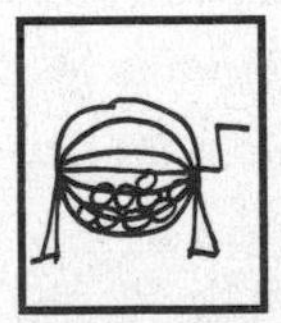

WIN THE LOTTERY

Skip Garibaldi MATHEMATICS, EMORY UNIVERSITY

One second you're standing at the 7-Eleven checkout counter with a Slim Jim and a Styrofoam cup of syrupy hazelnut espresso and the next second—BAM!—you're a gazillionaire! Hello château on the French Riviera!

That's the lottery.

The lottery's also a stack of one-dollar slips of toilet paper, which eventually leave you unable to afford Slim Jims and gas station coffee.

Assuming drawings actually are random, science can't help you pick the winning numbers. But, that said, some fiendishly simple stats can make the dollar you put down likely to win back that dollar and more. Here's how.

"Find a drawing in which the jackpot is unusually large and

the number of tickets is unusually low," says Emory mathematician Skip Garibaldi. The March 6, 2007, Mega Millions drawing reached a record $390 million; 212 million tickets were sold. Elaine and Barry Messner, of New Jersey, split the pot with truck driver Eddie Nabors, of Dalton, Georgia, who, when asked what he would do with the money famously said, "I'm going to fish."

But it was a bad bet.

Despite the massive prize, the huge number of tickets sold meant that a dollar spent on this lottery returned only $0.74 (versus $0.95 for roulette). In fact, Mega Millions and Powerball have never once been a good bet: Extreme jackpots generate extreme ticket sales, increasing the chance of a split pot—the average return on a one-dollar Mega Millions ticket is only about $0.55.

"But state lotteries don't get the same kind of press," says Skip. In rare cases, a state lottery jackpot will roll over a couple times without jacking ticket sales.

Here's the formula for finding a good lottery bet: Look for an after-tax, cash value of the jackpot that exceeds 0.8 times the odds against you, and in which the number of tickets sold remains less than one-fifth this jackpot. If this makes absolutely no sense or if you happen to be away from your spreadsheets, here's how to approximate the formula: Look for a jackpot that's rolled over at least five times and that remains below $40 million. It's a good bet that it's a good bet. And by a good bet, I mean a positive expected rate of return—over time, a dollar invested returns more than a dollar. To wit: a $1.00 ticket for the March 7, 2007, Lotto Texas drawing had an expected rate of return of $1.30. That rocks.

Take a minute to scroll through online lottery listings till you find one that meets the criteria for a good bet.

OK, OK, so you finally found one—what now?

Pick the most unpopular numbers, that's what. By playing unpopular numbers you won't win any more or less often, but you'll less often split the pot with other winners.

Don't pick the number one. It's on about 15 percent of all tickets. Similarly, avoid lucky numbers 7, 13, 23, 32, 42, and 48. Better are 26, 34, 44, 45, and especially overlooked number 46. Avoid any recognizable pattern, but give slight preference to numbers at the edge of the ticket, which are underused. In mathematical terms, picking a unique ticket makes the jackpot look bigger.

If players in a 1995 UK National Lottery drawing had played unpopular numbers, they might've avoided splitting a £16 million pot 133 ways. That's right—133 people picked the numbers 7, 17, 23, 32, 38, 42, and 48, all straight down the ticket's central column. Each got £120,000. Play smart over enough drawings, and eventually you'll win more than you spend. That is, if you don't run out of money first.

If you want to get deeper into the lottery thing, Garibaldi has accessible and not-so-accessible versions of the paper linked from his faculty bio.

Once you win the lottery, you'll certainly have more time to look deep into your conversation partner's eyes and know her true feelings, right? Wrong. In a series of studies at the University of California–San Francisco researchers found that people of low socioeconomic status were better than wealthier subjects at recognizing and interpreting others' emotions, including being better at predicting emotion from snapshots of eyes.

IMAGINE EATING TO EAT LESS

Carey Morewedge DECISION SCIENCE, CARNEGIE MELLON UNIVERSITY

Imagine M&M's. There's the crinkle of the bag, the tinkling sound of hard shells shifting inside; when you pop one in your mouth, a brief hint of sweetness as the shell starts to dissolve, followed by the meaty burst of chocolate. Do you let the shell melt slowly or do you crunch immediately into the center?

I bet your mouth is watering (mine is . . .). I bet you'd really like an M&M right about now (I do). And according to Carey Morewedge, decision science professor at Carnegie Mellon University, you should. "There's a long history of research showing that cues of desired stimulants—the smell or the thought of steak or cigarettes—sensitizes you to the stimulus," he says. A whiff or a remembrance makes you want it more.

Sure enough, when Morewedge had subjects imagine moving M&M's from one bowl to another, they then ate more M&M's from a bowl he gave them to snack on. They were sensitized—primed and ready to munch.

But when Morewedge had subjects imagine actually eating the M&M's, they then ate fewer when given the chance. The more candy subjects imagined eating, the less they actually ate. The same was true of cheddar cheese squares—subjects who imagined eating more actually ate fewer.

The lesson here is obvious. If you imagine consuming any specific food, you can inoculate yourself against gorging on it in real life.

Try imagining eating potato chips before sitting down with a bag to watch football. Or imagine eating Cherry Garcia before touring the Ben & Jerry's factory. Or chocolate chip cookies while baking them for your kids. In all cases, you'll be likely to eat less once temptation is at hand.

Is this because imagining eating makes you feel full?

To test this, Morewedge had subjects imagine eating either M&M's or cheese, and then offered them a cheese bowl. Only the subjects who imagined eating cheese ate fewer squares. So it's not a phantom feeling of fullness that keeps you from overindulging, it's that—as opposed to just cuing the food, which sensitizes you to it—imagining eating a food habituates you to it. One piece of cake is great, two is good, three is OK, but four is bad. And imagining you've already had a couple slices means that when you actually start eating, you're further into the downward trajectory of enjoyment.

"But the effect is undone when you're exposed to a different stimulus," says Morewedge. So if you're going to be tempted by potato chips you have to imagine chips. If it's ice-cream-and-movie night, you have to specifically imagine eating ice cream. If you go down the list of goodies at an upcoming Thanksgiving meal, when you imagine eating yams, you will overwrite the inoculation of having previously imagined eating stuffing.

But if you can predict a tempting food, imagine eating it—the more the better. Then when it's there in front of you, you'll eat less.

Speaking of the health benefits of the mind, a study at Harvard Medical School found that even when patients were explicitly told the drugs they were taking were placebos, devoid of active ingredients (in fact, the pill bottles were labeled PLACEBO), their health improvements far outstripped peers given no sugar pills. While more research is needed, the study's authors suggest that the "medical ritual" of taking pills—any pills—might be to blame.

USE RUBBER BANDS TO BE A RADICAL ROCK CLIMBER

Hugh Herr BIOMECHATRONICS, MASSACHUSETTS INSTITUTE OF TECHNOLOGY

Believe it or not, Hugh Herr is this book's lone representative of the Sports Hall of Fame. A prodigy rock climber, Herr lost both lower legs to frostbite, the result of three nights in -20°F temps stranded in a blizzard on Mt. Washington. After rehab, Herr built prosthetic feet and hopped back on the rock, not in an I-still-want-to-climb-even-though-I-really-can't kind of way, but with the intent of picking up where he left off—on a tear through the country's hardest climbs. He showed up at the steep granite cliffs of Index, Washington, with tiny wedges of rubber-covered steel attached to metal tubing, which he planned to use as "feet" on the notorious overhanging crack City Park, which despite a bevy of able-bodied suitors had previously seen only one ascent.

Three days later, Herr styled it. And he did so partly because his prosthetic feet let him do something that ordinary climbers couldn't—wedge his "toes" into the viciously thin crack in order to take weight off his arms.

Not only had his prosthetics allowed him to perform as well as other humans, they made him superhuman. And it's this lack of human-as-end-goal approach that Herr brings to his work at MIT. "About half the work we do is augmentative," says Herr, meaning that while he's designed some of the world's best replacement legs and feet, he also designs mechanics to be worn on healthy humans. These are the exoskeletons that futurists and sci-fi buffs have imagined at least since 1963 when the character Iron Man debuted in *Tales of Suspense #39*. Imagine being able to run for miles with a hundred-pound backpack or jump from a two-story building. Herr's exoskeletons will make both possible.

But even more awesome is a project that brings Herr's interests full circle. "We're in the process of building a spider suit that augments the human ability to climb," says Herr. Basically, the suit will be a soft and flexible second skin jacket, with strong latex webs at the joints. These webs hold the suit and thus the arms, hands, and fingers in a fully flexed position—as at the apex of a pull-up. "It's cool 'cause there's no power source," says Herr. Instead, the suit makes use of muscle power that's generally unused while climbing—your pushing muscles. To extend your arms above your head, you push to stretch these latex webs, and when you pull down, the bands contract to pull with you. "The bicycle was invented, and now we have the sport of cycling," says Herr, "and just like that, someday we'll have a new sport of power climbing or augmented running. Augmentative technology will allow humans to do things we haven't even imagined yet."

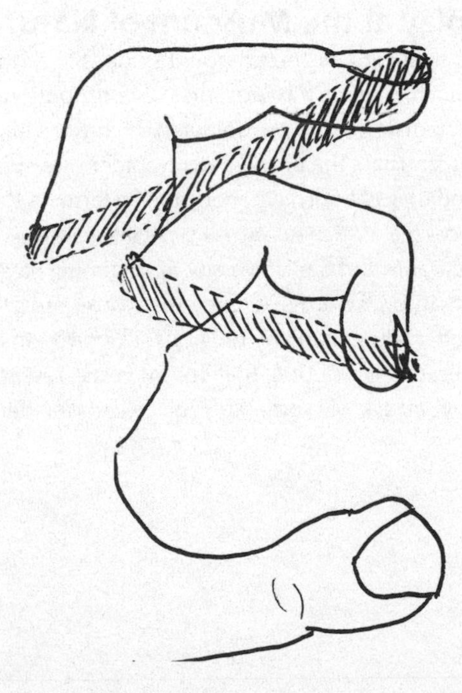

If you want a preview, as I most certainly did, try the following: Connect short lengths of surgical tubing from both shoulders to both hands so that you can only raise your arms with effort. Then stretch strong rubber bands from each fingernail to the base of each finger, as shown on page 53. The tricky part is keeping the bands in place, which I did with the liberal application of Super Glue (in the name of science!). Though only a rough prototype and admittedly pretty cumbersome, the bands made me immediately able to chuck mad dynos (translation: pull from hold to hold, not lob angry diplodocuses) at the climbing gym.

I'm sure that at least the gathered muscle-bound, knuckle-dragging college students thought it was pretty awesome.

On display at the Museum of Natural History is a 4' × 11' swatch of 96-thread-count spider silk cloth—as strong as steel and much tougher. It represents the contribution of more than one million female golden orb spiders, which were milked by hand in Madagascar. That's the problem with spider silk—spiders don't spin cocoons and they eat only live food, and so farming them for silk is nearly impossible. Which is why it's especially exciting that scientists from Notre Dame and the University of Wyoming have inserted spider genes into silkworms. Already the worms are producing stronger, softer fabric than any previous silkworms. In addition to textile applications (including bulletproof vests), researchers hope their new hybrid silk will someday replace cadaver-derived artificial tendons.

DECOUPLING "COMFORT" AND "FOOD"

Mark Wilson PSYCHOBIOLOGY, YERKES NATIONAL PRIMATE RESEARCH CENTER

"It's like you need X amount of good feeling in the course of existence and you can get it in different ways," says Mark Wilson, psychobiologist at Emory University and Yerkes National Primate Research Center. One way monkeys in his lab get this good feeling is through dominance in the social hierarchy. It feels good to be top rhesus.

But there's another way.

Wilson gave his monkeys banana-flavored pellets, much richer in sugars than their normal diet. As you'd expect, all monkeys liked the banana pellets—I mean, who wouldn't? But check this out: Monkeys at the top of the social hierarchy regulated banana pellets to keep their caloric intake roughly similar to that of their standard diet.

Subordinate monkeys didn't. They binged.

Specifically, while the dominant monkeys might opportunistically snack on pellets during the day, subordinate monkeys stayed up late into the night, stuffing their faces with sugary goodness. (Midnight ice cream, anyone?)

The explanation Wilson favors is that a sugary diet excites dopamine pathways in the brain. Dominant monkeys already get their dopamine fix from social interactions, while subordinate monkeys get none. So we're back to "X amount of a good feeling"—subordinate monkeys eat their way to the dopamine release that dominant monkeys get naturally.

Going human, Wilson posits that, "If you're much less than X, you're much more prone to addictions of all sorts—food, exercise, shopping, gambling, psychostimulants."

It's easy to see how this applies to something like diet. "It's the notion my grandmother talked to me about," says Wilson, "comfort food." The trick in losing weight is to find comfort another way—without the food. Simply, if you make your life happier, you'll be less driven to overeat.

A survey of 30,816 Europeans found that Danes are happiest and Bulgarians the least happy. Factors most responsible for happiness were younger age, satisfaction with household income, being employed, high community trust, and religious conviction. However, an unrelated study found that while short-term happiness rises and falls with a country's economy, long-term happiness has nothing to do with your country's wealth.

WRING AN EXTRA $20 OUT OF A USED CAR

Devin Pope BEHAVIORAL SCIENCE, UNIVERSITY OF CHICAGO BOOTH SCHOOL OF BUSINESS

Ted Williams entered the final two games of the 1941 season batting .39955. If he'd sat them out, the average would've been rounded up to .400, making him the first (and still the only) MLB player to bat the milestone. Manager Joe Cronin told Williams the decision to play and risk it or simply sit on the record was up to Williams, who famously said, "If I can't hit .400 all the way, I don't deserve it." He went six for eight in the season-ending double-header and finished with a .406 batting average.

"But many players make the other choice," says Devin Pope, behavioral scientist at the University of Chicago's Booth School of Business. Though no one's yet had the good fortune to confront the decision while camped at .400, many players have entered their last at bat with a .300 average. "More than 30 percent of those batters send in a pinch hitter," says Pope. On the flip side of the .300 fence, Pope explains that batters at .299 never send in pinch hitters—and they never walk. For better or for worse, players who go into their final at-bat with a .299 average swing, trying to get the hit that puts them over the .300 hump.

The same is true of the diamond market. "You can't find any .99-carat diamonds," says Pope. Dealers know their customers will pay significantly more for a 1-carat diamond than they would for a .99-carat one, and so cut the stones accordingly.

So too with SAT scores. If a student scores xx90—like 1,590 or 1,690—they're about 20 percent more likely to retake the test than someone who scored lower in the last two digits. Next time—certainly—they'll hit that next hundred-point marker!

Thanks to our irrational human brains, we value these milestones—a .300 hitter, a 1-carat diamond, an 1,800 SAT score—disproportionately more than if they were just a tick lower. This means that batters have incentive to ride the pine at .300 or swing for a single at .299, trying to get to the high side of a value fence and thus likely earn a higher salary after the next contract negotiation. Conversely, advertisers exploit the low side of the value fence, pricing a gallon of milk at $3.99 and a car at $19,995. To our brains, the savings looks much larger than it actually is.

This also means that every time your car's odometer gains a digit in the hundreds spot, it loses twenty dollars in resale value. Devin Pope showed that a car with 50,799 miles is worth twenty dollars more than a car with 50,800 miles. That's an expensive mile. But a car with 50,899 miles is still worth as much as it was at 50,800. In respect to miles, your car doesn't lose value smoothly—it ratchets downward with the hundreds digit.

The effect is a little stronger when you tick a thousand miles. That'll cost you $250. But, "while all the 10,000-mile marks were huge," says Pope, "it seemed like people caught on to the

100,000-mile game." Even with the human mind's inability to see $3.99 milk as $4.00, with used cars, it's too obvious that a seller is trying to unload a car just before it charts 100,000 miles, so the price starts dropping at about 99,900.

So if you're buying a car, your best deals will be just after it's hit a round number—following 50,000 or 100,000 is ideal. And if you're selling, make sure you do it before the car reaches those milestones that make it seem old. If that looming milestone is the big 100,000, sell it before 99,900.

Or at least before the odometer's last two digits roll from 99 to 100. It'll bring an extra twenty dollars.

University of Washington accounting researcher Dave Burgstahler found that businesses act very much like baseball players—if a company's camped just below the yearly break-even point, or an influential analyst's earnings prediction, or last year's profits, it'll swing for that fence. Unfortunately, this tendency also creates an incentive to indulge in "creative" accounting, similar to a ballplayer's morally questionable decision to send in a pinch hitter when batting .300.

HAPPINESS, WHY LAWYERS DON'T VOLUNTEER, AND HOW TO FUND A NONPROFIT

Sanford DeVoe ORGANIZATIONAL BEHAVIOR, UNIVERSITY OF TORONTO ROTMAN SCHOOL OF MANAGEMENT

Is happiness having the time to listen to milkmaids yodeling, smell the much-honored roses, and watch kittens doing whatever they do that everyone finds so ungodly cute on YouTube? Or is it cold, hard cash that lights your happiness lamp?

It depends on whether you're paid a salary or by the hour.

Sanford DeVoe, professor of organizational behavior at Rotman School of Management in Toronto, found that "people who think of time as money are more likely to rely on how much they earn when evaluating what it means to be happy." But this doesn't mean that the salaried are necessarily happier. Being paid handsomely by the hour makes you happier than if you'd earned the same amount from a salaried position. But if you're paid peanuts, it's better not to have your nose rubbed in the butter by highlighting a paltry hourly pay—you'd be better off salaried.

If you're a business owner, there's application here: Because time is money to those paid hourly, DeVoe found that hourly workers are much more likely to give up free time to earn more money. On the other hand, salaried workers take their vacations.

But here's a cool twist: Because hourly versus salaried pay affects how much you value your time, it also affects how you choose to spend your time. "Even outside lawyer jokes, this explains why lawyers don't volunteer," says DeVoe. He asked seniors at Stanford Law how many hours a week they volunteered, and then followed these greenhorn lawyers as they left school and got jobs in which they were either salaried or billed by the hour. After six months, he found their behaviors had changed—while both groups volunteered a bit less (presumably they were busier . . . or across the board more cynical), those who billed by the hour cut their volunteer hours more drastically than those who were salaried. Across professions and income, people paid hourly are 36 percent less likely to volunteer than those who are salaried.

In a follow-up, DeVoe asked the now battle-tested lawyers if they'd be more likely to volunteer an hour of their time at a charity of their choice, or if they'd rather write a check to the same charity for the money they made working for one hour. You guessed it: The salaried lawyers volunteered time, while the bill-by-the-hour lawyers wrote checks.

"There's a lot of personal utility you get from volunteering," says DeVoe, "but making lawyers aware of their hourly rate made them see volunteering as a purely economic decision, outside any personal utility factors."

Here's the obvious significance to your small community nonprofit: If you can guess how your prospective donors are paid, you can decide what to ask for. Should you ask for volunteer hours or should you ask for cash?

If you're hoping for the cash, take another tip from DeVoe. He had salaried people calculate their hourly rate before exploring their willingness to give money or hours. Sure enough—even the previously time-giving can be tricked into coughing up the cash by bringing time-is-money to the forefront of their minds.

So if your nonprofit needs cash (not volunteer hours), consider a donation flyer with a chart showing how common salaries convert to dollars-per-hour. Putting hourly wage at the top of donors' minds should help make them cough up the cash.

DeVoe and collaborator Chen-Bo Zhong showed that even subconscious exposure to fast-food symbols made people read faster and reduced their willingness to save money for a rainy day. In short, priming with fast-food symbols makes people impatient.

A Gallup survey of 153 countries found that a country's overall happiness was a better predictor of its population's charitable giving than was wealth. In overall giving, the United States ranks sixth, behind (in order) Australia, New Zealand, Ireland, Canada, and Switzerland. Interestingly, while people in poorer countries were less likely to give money, they were more likely than people in most richer nations to help strangers, with Liberians being the world's most stranger-friendly. In the United States, 60 percent of people had given money in the past month, 39 percent had donated time, and 65 percent had helped a stranger.

THE SCIENCE OF SPEED DATING

Paul Eastwick and Eli Finkel SOCIAL PSYCHOLOGY, TEXAS A&M UNIVERSITY, NORTHWESTERN UNIVERSITY

Social networking sites keep you connected with people you swapped sandwiches with in the third grade. Online forums let you argue about DIY lightsaber design with people on the other side of the world. And online dating sites offer the immediate ability to meet hundreds of local singles, some of whom are allowed to live near elementary schools.

But is it just me, or has it gotten much, much harder to meet people in the real world? Earbuds block even the nicety of "Hey, can I get a spot?" at the gym. iPhone Scrabble keeps people from accidentally meeting gazes across a crowded restaurant. And it's become impossible to tell the schizophrenic from those simply chatting on their cell via hidden mike.

Thank God for speed dating.

True, it's three minutes of resume-forward romance, but at least it's face-to-face, right? And being face-to-face suddenly changes speed dating from a cold comparison of data to a situation beholden to interpersonal psychology. Simply, there are things you can do in person to land a mate that are far beyond the reach of your Internet profile. Here's how.

First, "there's a lot to be said for being a liker—if you treat people agreeably, they treat you likewise," says Paul Eastwick, psychologist at Texas A&M University. "But there's a wrinkle when it comes to initial romantic attraction," says Eli Finkel of Northwestern University, Eastwick's coauthor. It turns out that speed daters who rate everyone highly are liked less in return. Finkel explains that unlike in platonic situations of work, play, and friendship, "In dating, liking everyone can come off as desperate."

The duo's research shows that rather than liking everyone, what predicts being liked in return is the difference between your baseline "like" and how much you like a specific person. When sitting across from your dream date, you want to show a "like spike." Unfortunately it has to be honest. "One thing that's fascinating is that people can tell so fast—whether the flavor of the liking is unique versus general," says Finkel. You can't fake unique attraction, but neither should you try to tamp it down when it wallops you. Showing someone they're special makes them like you.

A second cool trick comes from the world of embodied cognition, which is a much-studied form of subconscious crossover between actions and thoughts. For example, people excluded from a social group in a lab setting report the lab itself feels colder. Finkel and Eastwick also point to a study of the "attractiveness" of Chinese characters—subjects found characters more attractive when they pulled them toward themselves than they found the same characters when they pushed them away.

In the world of speed dating, embodied cognition means that you want to sit instead of rotate—you tend to like things you approach. Sure enough, Finkel and Eastwick showed that while women are overall pickier than men, if men stay put while women rotate, it shortens the pickiness gap. (Think about this in terms of gender stereotypes, in which men pursue and women are pursued.) So in addition to letting your "like spike" (as it were) show, find a speed dating situation that allows your sex to sit—dates will approach you and so will like you more.

Mining dating data—try saying that ten times fast. Now bask in the glory that is a truly massive data set, generated by millions and millions of online dating profiles and their click rates. First, men get more responses to their messages if they don't smile in their profile pictures. And $20,000 in salary compensates for an inch in height. (Online daters lie, adding an average of two inches and 20 percent to their true heights and salaries.) And there are good and bad words to use in messages. Netspeak like "ur" for "your" hurts message response, as do physical compliments including the words "sexy," "hot," and "beautiful." Instead use words that show interest that runs more than skin-deep like "awesome" and "fascinating."

Puzzle #4: Matchmaker

You're the benevolent facilitator of a speed dating session. John, Jake, Jeremy, and Justin arrive to meet Emma, Ella, Eliza, and Eva. As per regulations, they all chat and then they all score each other—er, evaluate each other. If the chart below shows these scores (girls' evaluation of guys on the left, and guys' evaluation of girls on the right—the higher score the better), how should you pair these love-struck contestants in order to create the most overall happiness?

	Emma		Ella		Eliza		Eva	
John	3	9	7	7	2	6	4	7
Jake	9	9	1	5	1	6	9	3
Jeremy	2	9	6	6	5	8	4	2
Justin	5	7	3	4	4	5	3	2

HOW TO BE A BALLER

John Fontanella PHYSICS, UNITED STATES NAVAL ACADEMY

In the immortal words of rapper Skee-Lo, do you wish you were a little bit taller? Wish you were a baller? Wish you had a girl who looked good and you would call her? Wish you had a rabbit in a hat and a bat and a '64 Impala?

It's a lengthy list.

John Fontanella, physicist at the US Naval Academy, can help you with the second—being a baller, that is. He wrote the book on basketball, or at least on *The Physics of Basketball*, which you can use to light up the scoreboard regardless of height and/or possession of said Impala.

First, the basics. In homage to the Naval Academy, think about basketball as ballistics. You're blasting a projectile that travels up and then down, while also traveling horizontally, describing a parabola from your hand to the hoop (ideally). In basketball's case, the higher the arc, the more straight down the projectile travels as it nears the hoop, and thus the bigger the target looks (you already knew this). But the shortest distance between two points is a straight line and so the higher the arc, the longer the shot's total distance and thus the more precise it has to be leaving your hand (error is magnified over distance).

So there's an optimal angle of release—one that balances the desire to drop straight down at the hoop with the desire for a short, overall path. What's the balance? Another physicist, Peter Brancazio of Brooklyn College, used some nifty trig to show that due to the size of the ball and the surface area of the hoop, any angle shallower than 32 degrees hits the back of the rim. The angle that gives the most margin for error is 45 degrees plus half the angle from the top of the player's hand to the rim.

Imagine this angle: You're hanging in the air, hand extended—draw a line from your fingers to the rim. Now scoot this frozen-in-time jump shot closer to the rim. As the hand gets closer, the angle gets steeper, and as you move the hand out past the three-point line, the angle of the line connecting fingers to rim gets shallower. This makes the ideal angle of a shot from just beneath the rim almost straight up and a long-range jumper almost exactly 45 degrees. It also means that a shot released above the rim can be shallower still, subtracting half the angle between fingers and rim from the balance point of 45 degrees.

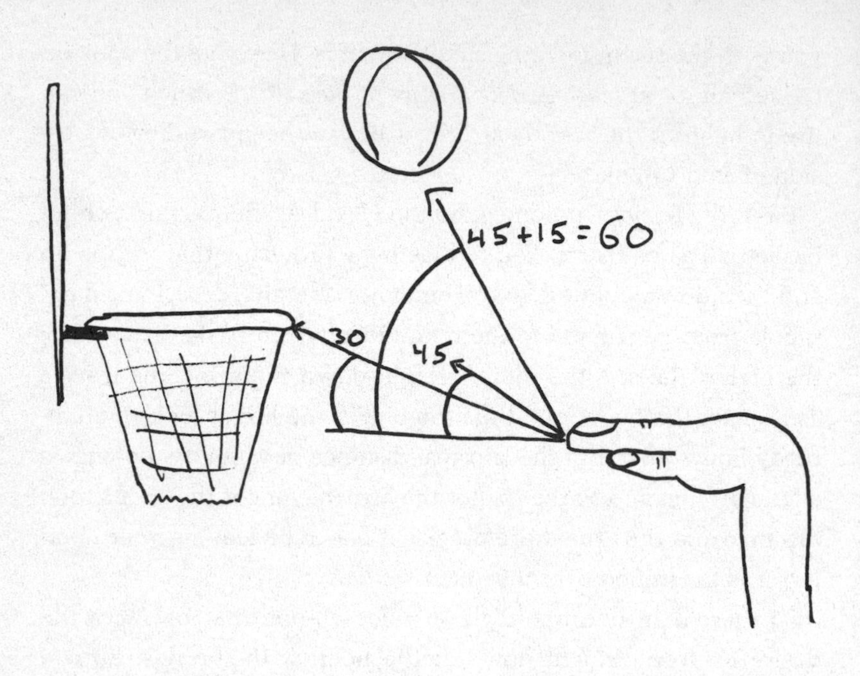

Practice it from different distances—a shallower shot from farther out, but assuming you're releasing from below the rim, never less than 45 degrees.

Another problem that Fontanella points to with a high-arc shot is that of approach speed. "A good shooter minimizes the ball speed at the basket," he says. "That's a soft touch." On the off chance that your perfectly angled shot catches metal, you want it to grab like a golf ball catching the green, bouncing around in the small, defined cylinder above the basket where it has the greatest chance of rolling in. And like golf, a big piece of a soft touch is backspin. Simply, it takes speed off the ball and keeps it in the cylinder.

Finally, with about 359 degrees around you where the ball won't go in the hoop and only about one degree where it will, randomness isn't in your favor. And any aspect of your shot that increases randomness is an aspect that hurts the chance of success. "The really good shooters do it the same every time," says

Fontanella. Good shooters land in the same place they took off, and they release the ball at the jump's apex, meaning they're traveling neither side to side nor up and down at the instant the ball leaves their hand. It's a perfectly still moment in time, with no random movement that creates drift. To see randomness in action without a jump, look at a Shaquille O'Neal free throw. The arm never travels the same path twice.

On the other end of the spectrum, if your memory can't call up a snapshot of Reggie Miller hanging in the air like a plumb bob with his shooting arm extended at 50 degrees, find a vid online.

That's how to be a baller.

Puzzle #5: Tramp Trouble

And with that geometric refresher, imagine the following dilemma: It's Christmas Eve day and the trampoline your in-laws shipped to you—which you'd meant as the holiday gift centerpiece—is too big for your condo's porch. But if it weren't for that darn support pole in the middle of your garage, the trampoline would fit in there easily. Hey, maybe it will still fit! Can you possibly, possibly somehow stuff a trampoline with a 12-foot diameter into the two-car garage shown on the next page, thus saving Christmas?

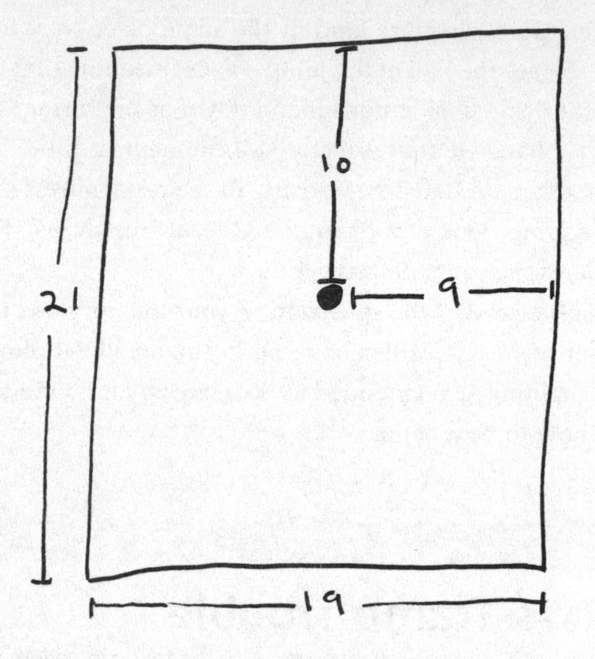

HOW TO PANHANDLE

Lee Alan Dugatkin BIOLOGY, UNIVERSITY OF LOUISVILLE

Why do bees give away meat or defend other bees at cost to themselves? Doesn't this behavior decrease the likelihood of Mr. Care-and-share bee passing on its let's-all-hold-hands-and-sing-"Kumbaya" genes? Doesn't evolution prune these pinko hippie bees from the genetic tree of life? "Altruism drove Darwin crazy," says Lee Alan Dugatkin, biologist at the University of Louisville and author of *The Altruism Equation*, "but the answer is deceptively simple."

Whether or not you help someone in need comes down to three factors: (1) how much it costs you to help; (2) how much the person gains by your help; and (3) your genetic relatedness to the person in need.

This is the altruism equation: $r \times b > c$. If relatedness times benefit outweighs cost, then you help. You'd throw yourself in front of a train to save two of your siblings or eight of your cousins, but not one of your sibs or seven of your cousins. This is because, on some level, you recognize that a sibling has half of your genes—saving two brothers passes on the equivalent of your genetic material. Same with eight cousins. Similar might be true of an airplane full of people of your ethnicity, or a cruise ship full of people from all over the world. Altruism makes sense "if you can somehow make up for the cost of being altruistic by increasing the chances that your genetic relatives survive and reproduce," says Dugatkin.

Anthropologist Napoleon Chagnon famously studied this relationship of altruism and kinship among the Yanomami of Venezuela. From the mid-1960s to late 1990s, when Chagnon lived with the Yanomami, they were into all sorts of nifty things like periodically banding together in ever-changing alliances to cut off heads, shrink them, eat people, etc. Chagnon almost lost his noggin more than once, but survived to compile extensive genealogies of the Yanomami, showing interrelatedness among the many widely dispersed tribal groups. And what he found is a clean (inverse) correlation between relatedness and the likelihood you'll chop off and shrink someone's head and/or eat them. Even without prior knowledge of kinship, the Yanomami somehow knew not to eat family.

"I think the human psyche has been designed to pick up clues that come from gene expression," says Dugatkin. Certainly, studies have shown that we're very, very good at recognizing people we're related to, even without having met them before. What cues this recognition? Is it genetic? "Even the evolutionary biologists are trying to develop models of culture in which the gene is not the central player," says Dugatkin, "but this thing called a meme that represents information is the unit that selection operates on."

So, the theory goes, when we instantly recognize a long-lost relative in a lineup, it's not that we somehow intuit this relative's genetic makeup—it's that we similarly intuit memes, or the many signals not only of genetics but of cultural similarity, including Aunt Joan's clipped "T's," Great Uncle Wilbur's habit of winking as punctuation, and Grandpa Gary's bad sense of humor that makes one pepper terrible puns throughout a book of scientific tips.

This reliance on memes rather than genes to determine relatedness bodes well for your ability to fool others into being altruistic toward you—to, for instance, make them give you money—for while it's rather cumbersome to change your genetic structure to be more similar to that of a person you're hitting up, changing your memetic structure—the ways you signal genetic similarity—is totally doable. "There are ways to create the illusion of genetic relatedness among people," says Dugatkin. "Look at the military or religious organizations referring to people as brothers." This language creates false kinship . . . and people in these organizations help one another.

Further evidence for the power of kinship language comes from another sort of evolution. How many lines do you think a panhandler tries in a career of begging? And why do you think some lines become more used than others? Because they work, that's why—the others are selected against. And what's the stereotypical, clichéd panhandling line? It's "Brother, can you spare a dime?" By implying relatedness, the panhandler thumbs the scale of the altruism equation and makes it in your genetic interest to give (remember: Relatedness times benefit must outweigh cost).

And if you're going to try to get money or other aid out of a population, you'd do well to walk like them and talk like them too. "We use similarity as a proxy for kinship," says Dugatkin, "and the slightest indication of relatedness can stimulate altruistic behavior." If you want money from your uncle, be sure to use Aunt Joan's clipped "T's" when making your request.

So you can influence the perception of relatedness.

Next let's look at cost (again, not to beat it over the head or anything, remember: $r \times b > c$).

You know the saying "It's better to give than to receive." While this is so obviously parent-speak for "For God's sake just give your little sister the My Little Pony Tea Set!" it contains at least an element of truthiness. That element is the fact that we can gain by giving. A person might not gain money by giving you a dime (or they might, in the long run, due to reciprocity, but that's another long scientific story), but instead they might gain the admiration of a date, or giving a dime might allow your target to feel like a swell fellow. Or hold a sign that gives a laugh in return, like NINJAS KILLED MY FAMILY. NEED MONEY FOR KUNG FU LESSONS! Or think of the broader meaning of "cost." To a well-dressed woman in a business suit, a dollar may have the same "cost" as a dime to you and (especially) me.

Or think about the perceived worth of money: A quarter seems useful, while a dime is the first denomination that, for whatever reason, seems worth less than its face value. In other words, it seems like it costs $0.35 to give a quarter, while it only costs about $0.07 to give a dime. We're back to the logic of "Brother, won't you spare a dime?"

Finally, it also matters how much this dime would benefit you. Imply that it will save your life or at least provide the tipping point into something tangible like a sandwich or a bed or a beer, and you're more likely to get what you need.

So if you're asking for anything—your boss for a raise, your parents for a car, or a stranger for a handout—imply relatedness, decrease the cost of giving, and promise massive personal benefit to tip the scale of altruism in your favor.

In his book *Mr. Jefferson and the Giant Moose* (surprisingly, not a children's title), Dugatkin tells the story of the French notion that the fledgling United States was populated by underevolved, inferior, weakling species. To counter this ethnocentric arrogance, Thomas Jefferson had the skeleton of a seven-foot-tall moose shipped first-class from New Hampshire to Paris.

Researchers at Washington State University found that across a number of studies, instead of applauding people who contributed more than their fair share to a group while taking little in return, other group members wanted to kick the do-gooders out entirely. Reasons include making others look bad, setting an example that others would rather not have to follow, and simply acting contrary to established social norms. So if you're a natural angel, find a little devil to express or risk being shunned.

HOW TO TAKE A CORNER

Charles Edmondson PHYSICS,
UNITED STATES NAVAL ACADEMY

At the end of the day racing comes down to what you've got under your hood, right? Not necessarily. When I chatted with Charles Edmondson, physicist at the US Naval Academy and author of the book *Fast Car Physics*, he was fresh back from the track. The truck with his fast car on it hadn't started, so he'd been forced to borrow a friend's Neon. Edmondson, who's also an instructor for road-legal racing, said, "Even with this tiny little four-banger econo-car, I was able to run down all the students in the intermediate group, including a guy in a turbo Porsche."

This is because straightaway speed isn't the crux of racing. It's how you take a corner that counts.

"Friction's a finite resource," says Edmondson. It's this friction of rubber meeting the road that keeps your car connected to and thus turning around a corner. And using any of this limited friction to brake takes away from the friction available to turn. "Experts do 80 to 90 percent of their braking before they hit the corner," says Edmondson. Allotting all possible friction to turning instead of braking allows a higher max speed before skidding.

And tires are a neat little physics problem—sure they're spinning, but as each little panel of the tread hits and grips the road, it becomes momentarily static in regard to the pavement. Because this static friction (the grip something has while sitting still) is so much greater than tires' kinetic friction (the grip something has when it's already sliding), the consequence of a small slip tends to be pretty spectacular—a tiny skid slashes a car's friction limit from static (high) to kinetic (low) and the slide is off to the races, as it were. Commence catastrophic failure and general fiery badness.

But braking early isn't the end of the story. Next you want to take a racing line. Imagine you can hug the tight inside of a curve or you can go high, riding the curve's outside arc. Which is best? It turns out it's nearly a wash—on the inside arc, you're forced to go slower but the arc is shorter overall; on the outside arc you can go faster but you also have to go further. Either way, you get to the end of the curve at pretty much the same time. So instead of taking the radius your lane gives you, "open up the radius of the turn as much as possible," says Edmondson. This means starting the turn high, tagging the low point of the inside corner, and then exiting the turn high.

It's the same in baseball. Frank Morgan, a math professor at

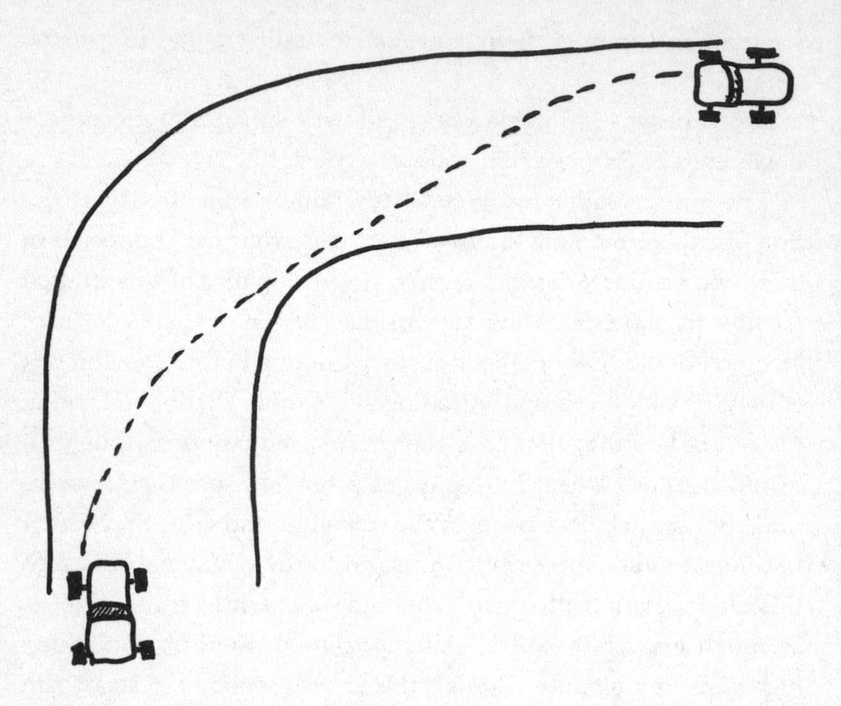

Williams College, showed that if you know you're going for second, you should immediately widen your path to first to the right of the baseline, allowing you to open up the radius of your turn around the base.

For a single turn, that's it: Brake before the turn and draw a kind arc.

But now imagine you're in an S turn (or any set of multiple turns). Exiting the first turn high brings you into the second turn low. That's bad. And if you're at your friction limit in the first and late recognizing the danger of a sharper turn in the second, braking only eats up that last little bit of friction, sending you over the static/kinetic threshold and into the wall. That's really bad.

So the best you can do among multiple turns is to prioritize the tightest turns—set up high coming into tight turns by taking nonoptimal lines on the wider turns.

That is, unless you have a straightaway coming up after the last

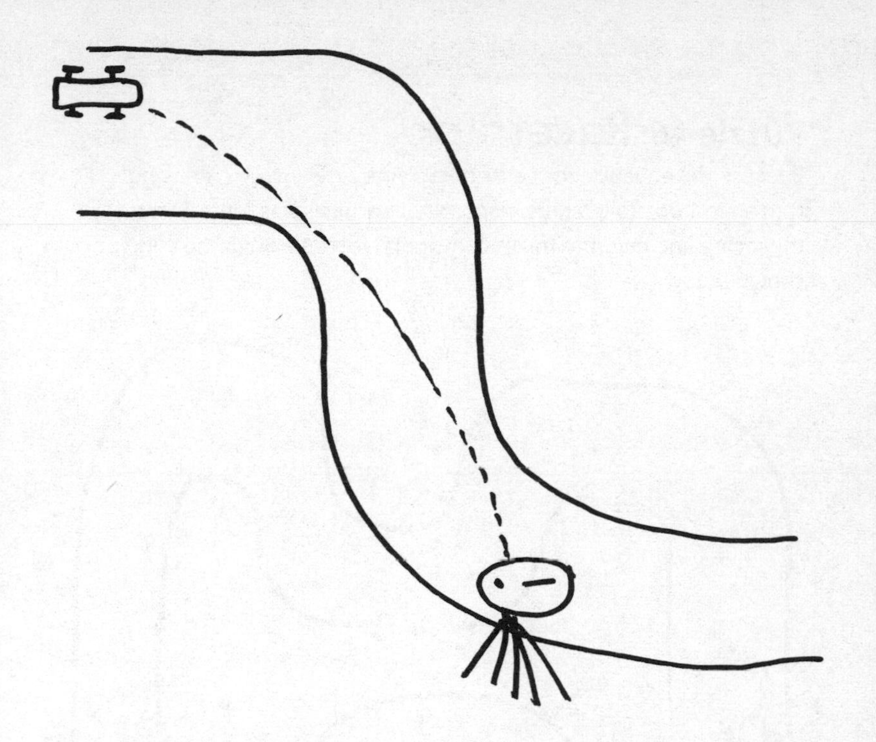

turn in a set. Because you want to travel as fast as possible over the longest distance possible, you should prioritize this last turn in the set so that the impact of your higher exit speed is magnified across the entire length of the following straightaway.

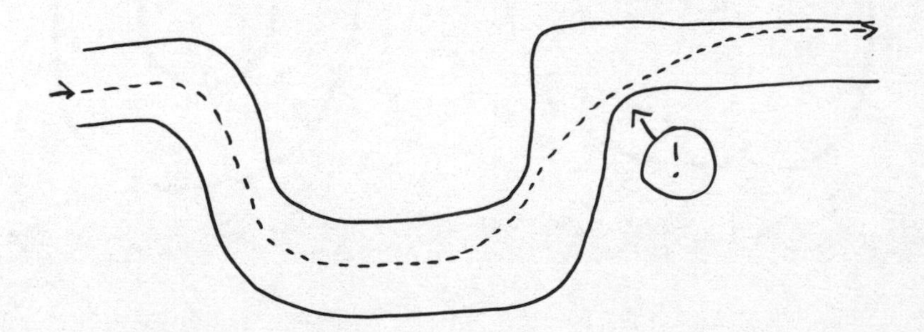

Puzzle #6: Racetrack

Because the equation for centripetal force is $F = mv^2 \div r$, drawing the longest possible radius means your car feels less force. Draw the racing line that minimizes centripetal force through the course shown below.

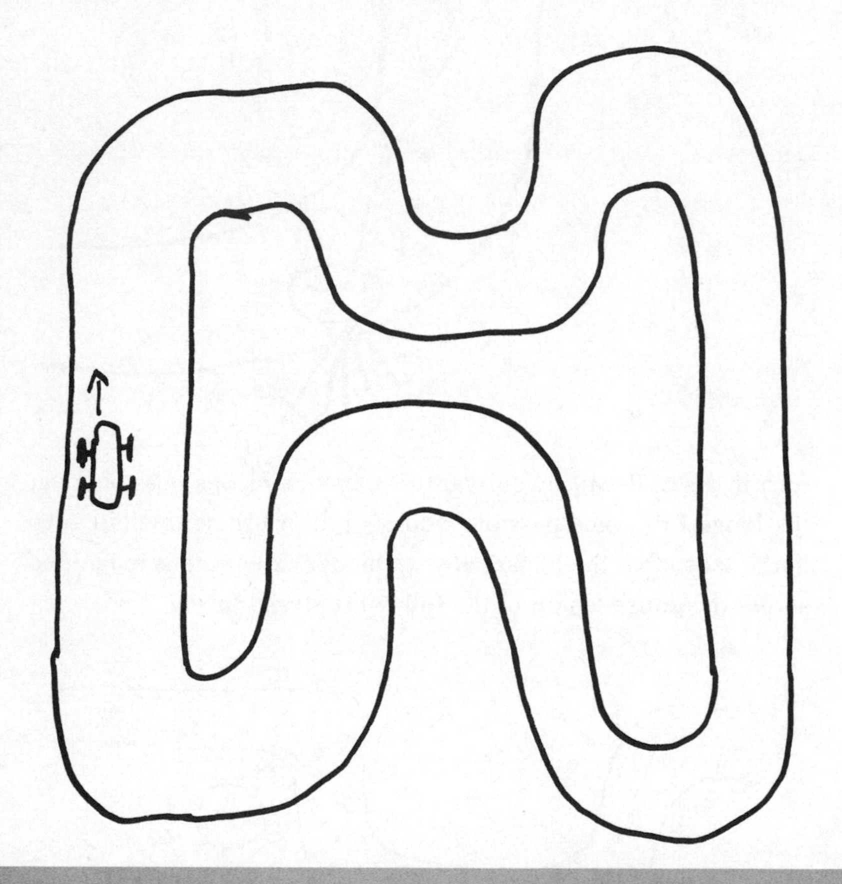

DESTROY STUFF WITH AWESOME SUPERVILLAIN POWERS

Steve Strogatz MATHEMATICS, CORNELL UNIVERSITY

Is Superman cool? No. He's a do-goody Boy Scout in tights and a codpiece. You know who's cool? General Zod, that's who.

And you can be too.

The easiest thing to destroy with your bare hands is a bridge: They swing.

Like London's Millennium Bridge, which, under the weight of six hundred people on opening day, June 10, 2000, started to boogie aggressively. There was no wind. And the people weren't marching in lockstep . . . at least not at first.

Then, as you can see in the Internet video, "People spread their feet wide and started walking in this hilarious Ministry of Silly Walks kind of way," says Cornell mathematician Steve Strogatz. Imagine standing in a rowboat. It starts rocking. What do you do? You spread your feet and go with the flow. "And they actually got in step with the vibrations in a way that pumped energy into the bridge," says Strogatz. This is a positive feedback loop: Strogatz showed that even a slight wobble causes people to synchronize in a way that creates an ever-increasing wobble (causing more people to synchronize, etc.).

And soon synchronicity of disastrous proportions arose spontaneously from randomness, with six hundred people pumping the Millennium Bridge like a swing, while the queen watched in horror.

But what created the first wobble? There are a couple theories, but Steve Strogatz chalks it up to chance: Of the 600 people on the bridge, at some point 301 people put their left foot down as only 299 put down their right. From there, positive feedback was off and running.

You can be that 301st person.

Good ol' Galloping Gertie, the Tacoma Narrows Bridge, ripped herself to shreds in 1940 due to aeroelastic flutter: She flapped in the breeze. But unless you were born on Krypton, you simply don't have the wind power for that kind of thing. Likewise, the Angers Bridge collapsed in 1850 when almost 500 French soldiers marching across the bridge accidentally matched its vertical resonant frequency. But engineers wised up and no modern bridge grooves to the vertical beat of human feet. If you want to crash a bridge, you'll have to swing it.

CREATE A CULTLIKE POSSE OF WORSHIPFUL AUTOMATONS

Eli Berman ECONOMICS, UNIVERSITY OF CALIFORNIA–SAN DIEGO

Once you have supervillain powers, you'll need an army of henchmen. Don't have one? Don't worry! Science can make one for you.

All you have to do is solve the problem of loyalty.

All organizations struggle to keep people: You help an employee cut her teeth in the business, but the second a more attractive offer comes along, she blows town. Businesses control defection with counteroffers and promotions. But admit it—you're too cheap to buy a posse. The Mafia has ways of dealing with defection too. But you need the trunk of your car for groceries.

And so the best way for you to keep a posse is with the tried-and-true method of Hamas, Hezbollah, the Taliban, and al-Qaeda: "All of today's successful terrorist organizations require a signal of commitment," says University of California–San Diego economist Eli Berman.

This up-front signal of commitment must outweigh the potential gains of later defection. For example, the initiation rite for the Hells Angels includes being peed on by the rest of the gang and then wearing your soaked leathers for a month. Once you've spent a month wearing the urine of large, hairy men, the cost you've paid to enter the club is higher than any potential gain you could earn by later defecting from it.

Cool: cost of initiation must outweigh potential gains of betrayal.

But what about recruiting your posse in the first place? There's another thing these top four terrorist organizations—Hamas, Hezbollah, al-Qaeda, and the T-ban—have in common: "They all started as mutual aid societies," says Berman. They provided services in communities that lacked them. And with limited resources, clubs had to learn how to be exclusive—they developed and tested initiation rites as signals of commitment, and wove club membership deeply into communities, families, and the fabric of culture.

Contrast this with the would-be terrorists known as the Toronto 18. They played soccer together—oh, and plotted the beheading of the Canadian prime minister. Word leaked and soon the group accepted a new member, Mubin Shaikh—a police plant who hung out until gathering enough evidence to arrest the lot of them.

Their downfall? They didn't require a signal of commitment, and their connection to each other was topical, rather than growing from mutual support ingrained in culture.

What this means for your posse is this: first, make yourself indispensable in a benign way, creating an exclusive club with membership benefits. Then require a stout initiation rite.

Only then will you have snitch-proof henchman capable of carrying out your supervillainy.

Can you guess how Eli Berman recommends squishing terrorist organizations? "Competent governments must provide social services," he says, thus removing the need for independent aid societies—the societies that can so successfully turn violent. Eli Berman is the research director for international security studies at the Institute for Global Conflict and Cooperation, and author of the extremely cool book *Radical, Religious, and Violent*.

Do you want to find a friend of a friend who plays cricket, World of Warcraft, and speaks Cantonese? Ask V. S. Subrahmanian of the University of Maryland, who created an algorithm that mines online social networks like Facebook. Or maybe you want an entrée into a terrorist network? Dutch researchers defined the mathematical signatures of likely terrorists within large, online social networks, and Subrahmanian now knows how to find them.

BUILD A CYBERNETIC THIRD ARM

Yoky Matsuoka BIOROBOTICS, UNIVERSITY OF WASHINGTON

If you want a smart third arm for diapering or dueling or gourmet cooking, MacArthur genius and University of Washington biorobotics expert Yoky Matsuoka can attach one directly to your brain.

"We go anywhere from skin contact to something that goes on the surface of muscles to brain surface interface to opening up the skull, peeling off the skin, and sticking needles into the brain itself," Matsuoka says.

That's very cool: Robotic prosthetics can now attach directly to and be controlled by neurons. If you're down an arm, you can strap a replacement to the neurons that would naturally control the missing limb. Or if you're still in possession of a full set and just looking for that "wow" factor, you can hook a prosthetic to a random, excitable neuron and train the neuron to control the arm. Check out online footage of monkeys at the University of Pittsburgh MotorLab: after using a brain-connected prosthesis to eat an apple, one monkey brings the hand close so he can lick his "fingers."

The question is, how much autonomy do you allow in your third arm? "We're going to have to warm up to the idea of letting the robot do more," says Matsuoka. That's because brain control is still a bit crude. And so instead of an arm that you instruct to pick up a Stratocaster and push each fret at exactly the right millisecond, it's easier to leave some "smartness" or degree of control in the prosthetic: Your brain may initiate "play guitar solo from Danish glam band White Lion's 'When the Children Cry,'" but then it's simpler to let the limb do it independently than it is to leave your brain in control.

Is that a bad thing? OK, in the preceding example it probably is—with or without a third arm, there's no excuse for wanting to play the guitar solo from "When the Children Cry." But in terms of robotic autonomy versus human control, ceding volition to robot overlords isn't a new thing. We already allow robot autonomy in devices like dishwashers, garage door openers, and Little League pitching machines—once we give the command, they automatically do the work. Would it be so wrong or even so different to "hijack a couple neurons," as Matsuoka puts it, and attach these machines to our brains rather than pushing buttons with our hands?

Puzzle #7: Dismembered Zombies

Oh no! The zombies below have become inconveniently dismembered! But even a zombie missing one limb is viable. How can you combine the pieces below to create the most viable zombies? Assume right and left limbs are not interchangeable, you can't double up limbs, bodies, or heads, and you have no access to a chainsaw, axe, or other tool of further dismemberment.

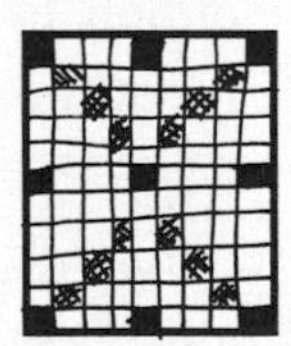

BE A SCRABBLE JEDI

Jason Katz-Brown QUACKLE, GOOGLE

"Here's the story of the only truly awesome play I've ever made," says understated Jason Katz-Brown, former US #1-ranked Scrabble player, and cocreator with John O'Laughlin of the gold-standard Scrabble site Quackle (www.quackle.org). "There were two tiles left in the bag and I was down by, like, a hundred points, holding E-G-I-N-S-Y-Blank." There are a lot of bingos he could've played from this bunch—words that use all seven tiles and thus score an additional fifty bonus points. "But it wouldn't have mattered," he says, "because next turn my opponent could've scored more points," and Katz-Brown would've been stuck playing catch-up again, with only the two tiles he drew from the bag as ammunition. He computed or intuited the odds—exactly which, he's not sure—and realized that his best play was to pass and ditch his E in hope of getting a higher-value letter that would allow him to bingo out. He drew a P, for G-I-N-P-S-Y-Blank. His opponent played and drew the only remaining tile, a J. Playing off a G on the board, Katz-Brown bingoed out with "gypsying," which my spell check doesn't like, but which is most certainly included in the *Official Scrabble Players Dictionary*. Not only did he bingo out big, but his opponent had to eat the J, swinging the score by another sixteen points. "I won by, like, a few points," says Katz-Brown. Lucky as it may seem, the thing is he foresaw this as his only chance.

I'm a casual Scrabble player, usually on my phone in bed at night, and I reciprocated with the very exciting story of my best play—the word "prejudice" off an existing "re" while playing against the computer a couple months ago. Katz-Brown was kind enough to pretend to be impressed.

This is to say that there are many levels at which Scrabble can be played. But according to Katz-Brown, the two basic tenets of good play are as applicable to me as they are to him: (1) know your words; and (2) be aware of the likely value of letters you leave in your rack. This is how Quackle computes word score—points plus leave value—and Katz-Brown says that when he sets Quackle to play only according to these two parameters, it can beat all but the best human players.

First, the words. After his freshman year at MIT, Katz-Brown took a summer internship in Japan (where he now works for Google). "And instead of taking advantage of, you know, Japan," he says, "I'd go back to my room and spend all night learning words." That summer, he learned all the words in *The Official Scrabble Players Dictionary*.

Let's imagine you're not going to do the same. Is there a way to get better at Scrabble with minutes—rather than months—of memorization? If you only wanted to spend time learning a handful of words, which should they be?

To find out, Katz-Brown and O'Laughlin had Quackle play itself thousands of times and looked for the best words. But these aren't simply the highest-scoring words; rather, they're the ones that allow the most advantage over other words you'd play with the same rack if you didn't know the big kahuna. For example, with an opening rack of E-H-O-P-Q-R-T, the best word is "qoph" (valued by Quackle at 46.6) and the second best word is "thorpe" (at 24.8). There's a big difference for knowing "qoph," and so it has high "playability."

In order of playability, the top forty words you absolutely must know are: qi, qat, xi, ox, za, ex, qis, ax, zo, jo, ja, xu, qadi, qaid, of, oo, if, oe, io, qua, yo, oi, euoi, oy, ow, wo, yu, fy, ee, joe, aw, we, zee, oxo, exo, axe, ye, fa, ou, ef. The first bingo on the list is "etaerio." You can find the full list with a quick search for "O'Laughlin playability."

Now to leave values, which are a bit more esoteric. Sure, it's nice to score points. But it's also nice to set yourself up to score points next time. This is what you do when you play tiles that leave compatible letters in your rack. Again, Katz-Brown and O'Laughlin engineered massive Quackle-on-Quackle action to discover the combinations that predict success on the next turn. If you're going to keep only one tile, best keep the blank (notated "?"), followed by S, Z, X, R, and H. Many of the same suspects show up in two-tile leaves, with the best being ?-?, ?-S, ?-R, ?-Z and the first without a blank being S-Z. If you're leaving three tiles, none of them blank, oh please let them be E-R-S! Other great three-tile leaves are E-S-T, E-S-Z, R-S-T, and E-R-Z. And it's likely worth ditching one letter if you can leave A-C-E-H-R-S, E-I-P-R-S-T, or E-G-I-N-R-S. You can find full lists by searching for "O'Laughlin maximal leaves."

To demonstrate the power of leave values, Katz-Brown suggests imagining an opening rack of A-E-P-P-Q-R-S. "There's no bingo, and there's no obviously exciting play that scores a lot," he says. So what should you do? Despite Q's high points and what Katz-Brown describes as most players' "animal fear of having two of the same letter in your rack," the best play is to exchange the Q. With A-E-P-P-R-S, drawing any vowel will allow you to bingo next turn.

Data generation to solve specific questions? While Katz-Brown is the only person in this book without a PhD, knowledge creation through experimentation sounds suspiciously like science to me. There you have it: Scrabble solved with science.

"I can only define the two-letter words," says Katz-Brown, which puts him two letters ahead of most players in the world's top Scrabble country, Thailand, where players generally memorize acceptable and unacceptable letter patterns without connecting these patterns to words or meanings. At the yearly bigwig tournament in Thailand, Katz-Brown describes being mobbed by groupies for pictures and autographs. This, he implies, is somewhat different than the way top Scrabble players are treated in the United States.

Puzzle #8: Bingo! (Scrabble)

What five bingos can you make with the letters E-A-S-T-E-R-L?

GET YOUR SPOUSE TO DO MORE HOUSEWORK

George Akerlof ECONOMICS, UNIVERSITY OF CALIFORNIA–BERKELEY

In a 2000 paper that Google Scholar shows cited 1,683 times and counting, Nobel Laureate and Berkeley economist George Akerlof writes that in married couples, "When men do all the outside work, they contribute on average about 10 percent of housework. But as their share of outside work falls, their share of housework rises to no more than 37 percent." In other words, even when the wife is the primary breadwinner, she's likely to also do more of the housework.

But why? Assuming spouses have equal bargaining power, they should settle on equal "personal utilities"—when utilities are out of whack, bad feelings ensue and to heal this rancor, fairness must be restored. So why do relationships in which the wife works more reach equilibrium when she also does most of the housework?

"Actually, it's simple," says Akerlof. "The idea is that in any situation, people have a notion as to who they are and how they should behave. And if you don't behave according to your identity, you pay a cost."

In this model, the red-blooded American male takes a hit to his identity when his wife earns more money than he does, and a further hit when he does housework (the size of the hit commensurate with how much he's internalized the identity of "red-blooded American male"). To bring the "utilities" of husband and wife back into balance, she does more housework.

Similarly, if you adopt the identity of "host," you maximize your utility by serving drinks, and if you adopt the identity of "life of the party," you maximize your utility by consuming them. And within us are many, many identities—maybe you hold within you the identities of father, husband, rock climber, professional speaker, Grateful Dead fan, and author, each to varying degrees and thus with different bonuses and penalties to identity and personal utility for acting certain ways in certain situations. (At a speaking gig, I'm unlikely to pick an audience member to fence with a foam sword, but in my capacity as father . . . well, you get the point.)

Identity bonuses and penalties also explain why soldiers charge machine gun nests, while wussified authors of pop-science books can't imagine making the same decision in identical circumstances. Simply, the Army builds in recruits the identity of "soldier" and then the decision whether to charge is a balance with the chance of death sitting on one side and identity sitting firmly on the other. What's the greater penalty: the chance of death for charging or the identity loss for cringing? If the Army's done its job well, identity expectations of "soldier" overrule risk.

The same is true of schools and businesses. Organizations that help members adopt the identity of "student" or of "employee" create behaviors that would otherwise be illogical: Students learn; employees work. Akerlof also points to marketers of Marlboro or Virginia Slims cigarettes, who imply that to earn the identity bonus of "real man" or "sophisticated woman" you should set fire to and inhale their products.

Again, we act according to the social expectations of our identities or we pay a very real, tangible cost in personal utility. "The point is that you can socially engineer these things," says Akerlof. Witness the Army, a good school, a good business, or good cigarette marketers.

If you want your spouse to do more housework, you too will learn to socially engineer these things. There are exactly two ways to do it. First, you can encourage your spouse to modify his or her identity. Social scientists have known for years that identity is influenced by surroundings. In fact, Akerlof points to this sculpting power of culture as one of the (many) reasons poverty persists—by trying to transcend existing identity, a motivated teenager at a tough school forces identity penalties on all his or her peers. And so instead of applauding the motivated teen, peers tend to maximize the utility of their own identities by teasing away unwanted deviance. The use to you is this: Jumping directly into yoga class might be a stretch—no pun intended—but instead of nagging or cajoling or straight talk aimed at changing your spouse's identity, find situations—friends, classes, TV shows, magazines, etc.—in which culture will do the work for you. People who cheer with the team become more cheerleader-like. Your challenge is to find the right team.

Or you can frame the desired behavior so that it aligns with the existing identity. For example, if you're a wife trying to get your husband to put dirty clothes in the hamper rather than strewn around the floor near the hamper, how can you align this behavior with the identity of a real man? Is hitting the hamper like making the winning three-pointer? Is doing housework sexy? Does efficiently loading the dishwasher require manly spatial skills that only he can provide? Thus framed in terms of manliness, he can clean without paying an identity cost for it.

If you're a husband trying to get your wife to do more housework . . . well, shame on you. (That said, these techniques should work equally well.)

Akerlof is best known for his paper "The Market for 'Lemons': Quality Uncertainty and the Market Mechanism," for which he won the Nobel Prize in Economic Sciences. The paper addresses not fruit but used cars, and shows that because a buyer can never be certain of a used car's quality, it's more advantageous for sellers to put lemons than cherries on the market because prices converge toward an assumed low point. His newest book (with Rachel Kranton), which occupies brave new territory between the previous encampments of economics and sociology, is *Identity Economics: How Our Identities Shape Our Work, Wages, and Well-Being.*

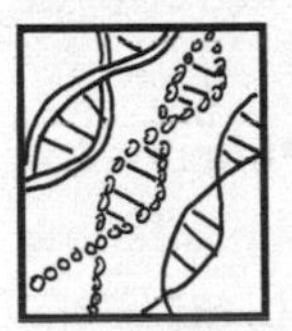

MAKE THE MOST OF THE GENES YOU GOT

Joseph Ecker GENETICS, SALK INSTITUTE

You know how it works. There are birds and bees. Daddy birds get together with mommy bees and they unzip their . . . chromosomes, throwing exactly half their genetic material into a pot. The stork, who's an old-school synthetic biologist, stirs the pot with his long beak, and out flaps the pair's unholy love child, feathers, stinger, and all.

Or something like that.

The point is this: Your child gets half its chromosomes from you and half from your mate. These form a tidy bundle known as a genome, and every cell in your child's body gets a copy. If you get a good genome, you'll be smart, beautiful, and happy. If you get a bad genome, you're doomed to a life of loveless and tormented bell ringing at the nearest cathedral.

Or something like that.

And in the wiggle room implied by "something like that" lies extremely cool and extremely new science. It turns out that while your genome is fixed, the expression of this genome is not. The software that controls this expression is the epigenome, and you can rewrite it.

On a basic level, "that's why we have eye cells and ear cells and every other kind of cell, despite the same genes in each," says Joseph Ecker, geneticist at the Salk Institute. It's said that a cook's only as good as his ingredients, but I'll tell you what: With flour, butter, eggs, milk, and caramelized bacon, the epigenome of Anthony Bourdain creates a very different meal than does the epigenome of Garth Sundem (which expresses only pork-flavored, unleavened pancakes).

So if you want to be smart, beautiful, happy, and cancer-free, the trick becomes not only reaching back in time to select super-parents and thus the right ingredients in your genome, but also convincing your epigenome to make the most of the ingredients it's got—to cook your genome like Bourdain.

Teaching your epigenome to cook depends on something called methylation. (Very) basically, attaching a methyl group silences part of a gene—in a cell that becomes eye tissue, all the other tissue types get the ball gag of a little methyl attachment, leaving only eye tissue to be expressed. When your eye cell copies itself to make more eye cells, it copies this methylation, too.

But over time, your DNA accumulates junk—viruses may insert snippets of Trojan code—and every time a cell duplicates itself, mutations may occur. So over time your genes generally get a bit messy. To avoid expressing the mess, you methylate everything you'd rather stayed quiet. It's like living in Maoist China, where you constantly jail potential dissidents.

And if you fail to silence the proletariat, your cells may rise up against you. We call this cancer. A mismethylated cell is unbound by its history, has no direction in life, and can and very well may party like it's 1999, leaving its directionless, cancerous progeny strewn about your body in places you wish it would not.

There are many drugs in the pipes to promote healthy methylation, troubleshoot mismethylation, and seek and destroy cells with the profiles of bad methylation. In fact, some of these are extremely promising alternatives to traditional chemotherapy. But until then, "there are bottles of folic acid on the shelves of Whole Foods," says Ecker.

The body's methyl comes from folic acid. Spread your folic acid too thin, and your epigenome doesn't have enough ball gags to silence the junk. That's why pregnant women take folic acid supplements—cells are duplicating at an abnormal pace and so need additional folic acid to keep pace with the epigenome's massive methylation. The same overtime cell duplication is true if you get a bad sunburn or otherwise cause tissue damage that needs big-time repair—your cells go into copying mode, and you need enough folic acid to ensure correct methylation of these copies. You know that sunburn causes skin cancer, and now you know why: increased chances for bad methylation.

But on the flip side, Ecker points out that taking too much folic acid may aid cancers in replicating out of control. In fact, some of the first cancer drugs were "antifolates" that stopped methylation and thus cancer cells' ability to reproduce.

So there are two things you can do right now, today, to ensure a happy epigenome: Please refrain from destroying your tissue and, barring that, take just enough folic acid to rebuild it properly. When you get a burn, pop a supplement but don't make it a habit.

Joseph Ecker and other extremely cutting-edge scientists are writing another chapter to the story of epigenomic effects. It turns out that in addition to rewriting your own epigenome and thus genetic expression through the way you live, you can pass elements of this rewritten epigenome to your children. For example, if you smoke before puberty, your grandchildren have a greater chance of reaching puberty early. And not only did Dutch mothers forced to near starvation during World War II have small babies, but their grandchildren were smaller too. Smoking and starving didn't affect genes, but it affected how the epigenome expressed them.

So to the age-old question of nature or nurture is added another player that splits the difference—keeping the epigenome happy through nurture affects the very nature of your children and grandchildren. So don't smoke, and eat right. Do it for the children. It's true we make a better day, just you and me.

Why be content to fiddle benignly with the epigenome when you can alter the very building blocks of life itself? Jim Collins, MacArthur genius and synthetic biologist at Boston University and Howard Hughes Medical Institute, inserted toggle switches into cells' DNA that "allows cells to flip on and fluoresce in the presence of certain chemicals or heavy metals," says Collins. These engineered cell mats are the new canaries in the coal mine. Then Collins inserted similar switches into yeast DNA, forcing the yeast to "commit cellular hara-kiri," says Collins, after counting seven days. Naturally—for example in beer—yeast can clump together before dying, but Collins's switches preempt this clumping and so can do away with the foul-tasting sediment in homebrew.

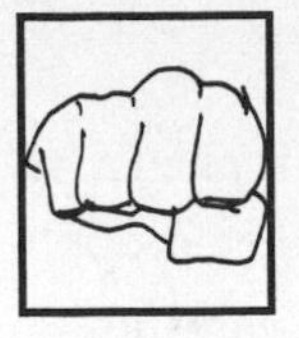

THROW A PUNCH

Jearl Walker PHYSICS, CLEVELAND STATE UNIVERSITY

"When I studied tae kwon do as a teenager, my master always told me to aim a forward punch inside my opponent's body," says Jearl Walker, Cleveland State professor and author of the classic book *Flying Circus Physics*. And when he got the professor gig, he decided to investigate why. First, he filmed himself throwing forward punches and then measured the distance his hand traveled each frame to discover where the punch reached maximum velocity. Sure enough, a punching hand is fastest at 80 percent of arm extension. After that, it's already slowing down to retract. Imagining a punch detonating behind the target's surface helps to ensure maximum speed on impact.

But max speed is only one of three factors that make the perfect punch. Imagine the superfast flick of your finger—it's annoying behind the ear, but it's unlikely to cause real damage. "What you want is maximum pressure," says Walker. This is high momentum applied over a small surface area, and it's why many martial arts teach striking with the side of the hand or the four pointy knuckles of your bent fingers—decreased surface area is like whacking a person with a stiletto heel instead of the sole of a sneaker. Ideally you'd punch with the fingertip of death, but unless you've trained for decades at a Shaolin temple, your one pointed finger is likely to crumple between your opponent's sternum and your onrushing arm.

In addition to speed and outside of adjusting your fist size, the best factor to focus on when throwing a punch is the third piece of pressure—mass. One reason a punch from a heavyweight does more damage than a flyweight's punch of the same speed is simple arm weight. A big wrecking ball does more damage than a little wrecking ball. "But an effective punch uses more than just the fist," says Walker. You've heard the phrase "Put your body behind it" and in punching that's exactly right.

"Rocky Marciano was an extremely effective fighter, partly because he was short," says Walker. Being shorter than his opponents allowed Marciano to punch upward, using his legs to add to the force of the punch—rather than bracing his punch against his weight alone. Speaking of bracing a punch against your weight, the wider your stance, the more horizontal force you can create. Likewise with a forward lean of your body—it's all about bracing your punch against the floor. For this reason, "what you see a lot of in movie martial arts—jumping up into the air—costs a lot of force," says Walker. By jumping you might gain the force that gravity exerts on your dropping body, but you lose the much greater force you could generate by pushing against the floor.

In fact, if you want to see the perfect punch in action, watch videos of Olympic shot-putters: a low crouch, a forward-leaning upper body, and a rotating torso, all with the aim of creating max force through one extended hand. A one-punch knockout comes from the legs.

Another punch researcher, psychologist John Pierce, at Philadelphia University, used sensors embedded in the gloves of professional boxers to measure punch force during matches. What he found is that while a one-punch knockout is certainly possible, much more common is knockout by accumulated force. "Once neck muscles fatigue, they can't absorb as much force, and so while later punches aren't necessarily thrown any harder, their force on the victim is much increased," says Pierce. He calls this point of neck muscle fatigue "the tipping point."

MAKE PEOPLE LAUGH

Robert Provine NEUROSCIENCE, UNIVERSITY OF MARYLAND-BALTIMORE COUNTY

Robert Provine played baritone sax with the Delbert McClinton band. He's also a neuroscientist at the University of Maryland-Baltimore County and wrote the book *Laughter: A Scientific Investigation*. From one to the other isn't the leap you might expect. "Good jazz and laughter are both products of listening to and responding to social signals," says Provine.

For example, take the opening of my recorded call with Provine—why do I laugh after saying, "Do you mind if I click RECORD? Because I'm thinking about podcasting quotes later . . . ha, ha, ha!" It's because I'm trying to signal that I'm no threat—to assure him that I won't stitch the quotes together into a Mel Gibson diatribe that I can then submit to celebrity gossip sites or otherwise use these recorded words against him.

Similarly, throughout the call, I chuckle to indicate understanding as in, "ha, ha, that's right!" And I laugh to indicate uncertainty, as in "I wonder if anyone's ever thought about that . . . ha, ha, ha?" Provine's spent thousands of hours cataloging similar uses of laughter, from campus gathering places to high school cafeterias to mall food courts. His findings include the facts that speakers are about 46 percent more likely to laugh than listeners, laughter is thirty times more likely in social situations than when alone, laughter frequently takes the place of periods or commas, and only 10–15 percent of prelaugh comments are even remotely funny.

"Actually," Provine says, "laughter is more about relationships than jokes." Human laughter evolved from the grunts and snorts of playing apes, who use these vocalizations to signal social inclusion. Sure, you may overlay the trigger of a punch line or a wry aside or a pun or a surprising observation, but if you want to bring the funny, you have to first become part of the pack. That's why so many jokes start with "There I was, standing in line at the grocery store," or "Don't you just hate airplane seats?," or other descriptions meant to create the bond of shared experience between joker and jokee.

"We don't laugh at Jay Leno because he's funny," says Provine. "We laugh because we empathize with Jay Leno."

So if you want to make people laugh, instead of practicing your punch lines, practice your empathy and listening skills.

Chris Ballinger of Magic Geek (www.magicgeek.com) points out that just like humor, magic depends as much on connecting with people as it does on trick mechanics. "Even when you buy a trick that's self-working, you need a story to make it magical," says Ballinger. He counts as his best trick a simple sleight of hand in which sponge rabbits multiply, saying, "the audience can be part of the story of these rabbits both physically and emotionally." Like humor, Ballinger says the crux of magic is "about being able to connect with the audience and fool them at the same time."

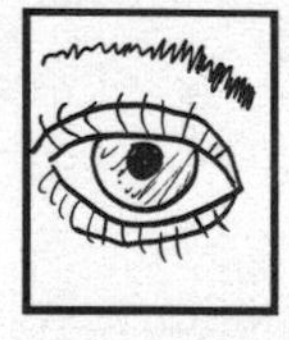

SEE UNHOLY COLORS

Jay Neitz OPHTHALMOLOGY, UNIVERSITY OF WASHINGTON

At your local Baskin-Robbins you might order a waffle cone dipped in chocolate with sprinkles, but cones in your eyes come in only three set flavors: S, M, and L. Each flavor of photoreceptive cone fires in the presence of a certain wavelength of light, and while there's some color crossover, effectively one recognizes red, another green, and another blue.

So your eye is like an RGB computer screen, with all the other colors of the rainbow a mixed twinkle of SLM cones firing in varying combinations.

That is, unless you're color-blind. Common red-green color blindness is caused by defective genes on the X chromosome, which code for whacked green cones—the wavelength these cones recognize is squeezed toward red, leaving green undetected. And because these bad genes are on an X chromosome, dudes without a backup X are especially susceptible—red-green color blindness affects 6 percent of males.

Jay Neitz hopes to change that. Neitz is an experimental ophthalmologist and head of the Color Vision Lab at the University of Washington, and he injected viruses into the eyes of color-blind monkeys.

Here's what a virus does: It attaches to a cell like a mosquito and injects genetic material. Commonly, viruses inject genes that appropriate the cell's machinery to create more viruses, which eventually rupture forth like battle orcs to continue the great cycle of viral life. But Neitz engineered his viruses to inject another kind of genetic material—genes that use a cell's machinery to make missing color pigments. (This, in a nutshell, is gene therapy. It's like downloading a software update.)

And—voilà!—these monkeys, once color-blind, now could see! One can only imagine their increased skill at discovering which guavas are ripe, and at driving amid traffic signals. Human application is in the pipes.

But why stop at bringing a deficit up to normal? (See this book's entry with Hugh Herr.) Why not keep a foot on the accelerator and blow right past the puny abilities evolution hath wrought?

"It's not a question of could," says Neitz. "It's a question of should." For example, he says, what about putting a light detector in your fingertip? Or creating a brain-linked array that would sense radiation or allow you to see heat? "It's hard to know what energies are out there we're not exploiting," says Neitz.

But even within the realm of existing senses, there's room for some good-natured, unholy augmentative technology reminiscent of creating a human-snake-meerkat chimera. For example, "What would a fourth type of photoreceptor be?" wonders Neitz.

Again, humans lacking the pigment needed to see green might mislabel yellow as orange or call a dark green car black. But what if we're all incapable of distinguishing, say, purple-quack from purple-not-quack, due to lack of a gene that codes for the quack pigment? What if instead of RGB we could see in RGBQ?

Personally, I'll take *Predator* vision, but seeing an inhuman color would be pretty awesome too.

While at the University of Wisconsin, Neitz consulted on a project that asked WDDS? After answering the question What do deer see?, it was a short step to creating more effective camouflage for human hunters. Interestingly, evolutionary biologists propose that the common red-green color blindness may actually help humans see through some types of jungle leaf patterns, making this color blindness an evolutionary advantage, especially for male hunters.

Speaking of supersight, neurobiologist Mark Changizi, formerly of Rensselaer Polytechnic Institute and now director of human cognition at 2AI Labs, has telepathy and X-ray vision. In fact, you do too. "We have an extra cone in our eyes that dogs don't have," says Changizi, and this cone is specifically calibrated to sense the minute color changes in skin due to hemoglobin oxygenation. "Human vision has not evolved to find ripe fruit in the forest," says Changizi, "but to sense emotions in others."

And about X-ray vision: "For a hundred years, they thought forward-facing eyes had something to do with stereovision," says Changizi, maybe allowing you better depth perception for jumping from branch to branch, grabbing fruit, and later chucking spears at passing mammoths and hitting balls of twine-wrapped cork. But there's a fairly glaring problem with that theory: Most animals that jump and catch have sideways-facing eyes. Instead, Changizi thinks forward-facing eyes are born of the forest. "Hold your finger in front of your eyes and you can see right through it," he says, pointing out that large forest animals with forward-facing eyes are equipped to see 6.5 times more stuff than forest animals with sideways eyes.

DRINK MORE TO EAT LESS

Brenda Davy NUTRITION, VIRGINIA POLYTECHNIC INSTITUTE

"The average American consumes two hundred calories of sugar-sweetened beverages every day," says Brenda Davy, health and nutrition researcher at Virginia Tech. Using the widely accepted (translation: debatable and vastly oversimplified) conversion of thirty-five hundred calories per pound of fat, this means that if you changed Pepsi into water, all else equal you would lose almost two pounds a month.

But Pepsi isn't the only thing you can replace with water. Water replaces food, too. And you don't even have to own enough willpower to consciously reach for a glass instead of a bite. Dr. Davy showed this by prescribing two cups of water before a meal. In the course of a twelve-week study, subjects who drank water before a low-calorie meal lost an average of five pounds more than subjects who simply ate the low-calorie meal.

In a yearlong follow-up to this study, Davy found that even with the removal of the low-calorie diet, people who drank water before meals were able to keep the weight off while people who went back to their lives as usual tended to gain some, most, or all of the weight back.

As an addendum to the first study, Davy had subjects rate their feelings of fullness and found that, sure enough, subjects who drank water felt more full. It's that simple: Drinking water takes space in your stomach you would otherwise fill with food. Interestingly, this means that the effect is weaker for younger people—gastric emptying rates are faster for the young, and so in a further test, by the time the meal was served twenty minutes after drinking water, not enough water remained in young stomachs to produce the effect. (If you're under thirty, consider chugging your two cups as you sit down to the table.)

But in addition to making subjects feel fuller, Davy thinks it's likely that drinking water before a meal functions as a psychological check-in with your weight-loss goals (see this book's entry on commitment devices with Katherine Milkman). The ritual of water before a meal is a gentle reminder to respect feelings of fullness.

HOW TO AVOID CAR THEFT

Ben Vollaard CRIMINOLOGY, TILBURG UNIVERSITY

"Car thieves are just like you and me," says Ben Vollaard, criminologist at Tilburg University in the Netherlands. "They seek to maximize gain and minimize loss." In other words, they're rational animals. Vollaard showed this by looking at car theft data before and after 1998—the year the Netherlands required that all new cars be equipped with an engine immobilizer, making hot-wiring nearly impossible.

Not surprisingly, with hot-wiring nixed, the rate of car theft plummeted. But the key fact here is that the immobilizers don't make stealing a car impossible. "You can still get a tow truck or download a program from the Internet that takes over a car's computer, but if you make it more difficult, crime goes down. It's an opportunistic behavior," says Vollaard. In this view, the thief walks down the street looking for a target whose value exceeds the risk and when he finds a car with the right balance, he looks up and down the block and jimmies the lock. And with engine immobilizers in place, risk went way up, making car theft less frequently a rational choice.

So if not a car, maybe a house? Not after the Netherlands wrote into their building code the requirement for burglary-proof doors and windows—houses built after the 1999 regulation are 25 percent less likely to be burgled.

What about a bike? In the case of cars and houses, the Netherlands employed a technique known as target hardening—making something more difficult to steal increases a would-be thief's risk and thus decreases the chance it will be stolen. In the case of bikes, they're trying something else: distorting the market to decrease a hot bike's value. New bikes in the Netherlands come with chips, and police have scanners. So with a wave of the magic wand, police can tell which bikes in the area are stolen. Who's going to buy a guaranteed police magnet? Instead of increasing risk by target hardening, putting a chip in a bike decreases the value of the stolen item, making theft similarly irrational.

Back to cars. The United States is one of the few countries in the developed world that hasn't yet required the engine immobilizer. (Don't tread on Detroit.) So you're still at risk. That is, unless you paint your car pink. Cyclists have done something similar for a long time—it's why the first thing you do with a sweet commuter bike is to paint it bland, scratch it up, and plaster it with stickers. Bikers call this "urban camouflage." Painting a car pink (or "distressing" a new bike) is like fitting it with a Dutch chip: It decreases its value—who's going to buy a pink car or a distressed bike?

Vollaard's DMV data shows that black cars are at highest risk for theft, perhaps because black looks the most luxurious. What was the theft risk for pink cars? Zero. Of the 109 pink cars in the study, not one was stolen.

If you want to keep your ride, paint it pink.

Now that you've avoided car theft, there are two more things you'll want to avoid: traffic jams and stoplights. Morris Flynn, mathematician at the University of Alberta, showed that at a certain overcapacity of cars on the road, following drivers don't have time to react to brake lights ahead, and so stomp their brakes harder than warranted, "and the information travels like a detonation wave through all the cars downstream of the braking," says Flynn—until everyone's stopped cold. Flynn calls these phantom jams "jamitons" and also showed that in these conditions, your best action—instead of stopping and starting with the flow of traffic—is to go at a uniform slow speed. You'll help the jamiton eventually clear itself, get to your destination just as fast, save gas, and decrease the chance of a crash-caused jam—one that can really put the kibosh on your timeliness.

As for stoplights, check out the video linked from computer scientist Peter Stone's faculty bio at the University of Texas-Austin of cars zipping through intersections, controlled not by lights and human drivers but by onboard computers. In Stone's autonomous intersections, car-mounted computers call ahead to an intersection "reservations manager" to reserve the milliseconds the car needs to pass through the intersection without becoming a twisted ball of plastic and metal. Then the onboard computer takes over to ensure the car drives through the intersection in its reserved time. "Technologically, it's feasible to do this right now," says Stone. "The barriers are the legal and insurance industries." A quick peek at the online video shows why—it's terrifying—but it does away with stoplight wait times almost entirely.

TO KNOW OTHERS, KNOW THYSELF

Julian Keenan NEUROSCIENCE, MONTCLAIR STATE UNIVERSITY

She says she's just a happy-go-lucky girl who likes loud music, a cold beer, and a guy in a cowboy hat.

He says what he'd really like to do is settle down and have a family.

What do you think the chances are that either's telling the truth? How good are you at spotting deception in the opposite sex? No matter your current skill, Julian Keenan, director of the Cognitive Neuroimaging Lab at Montclair State University, can make you better.

He knows because his lab stuck a host of female undergrads in front of videos showing guys being honest, guys playing good, and guys playing bad, and then looked at the personality and demographic characteristics of girls who were good at sniffing out naughty rats.

First, Keenan found that people who are more self-aware are better at spotting deception in others. (Note: this does not necessarily mean that by becoming more self-aware, you would increase your lie-detection skills. Beware the jabberwocky of correlation and causation.)

But check this out: Keenan also found that single women are much better than women in committed relationships at detecting male deception. While this may be a news flash, it makes sense from an evolutionary perspective: If you're in a long-term relationship, you no longer need to be as edgy around guys who could very well be talking a big game about love and family and commitment in hopes of winning a one-night stand. You're not only out of practice but also lack the proper motivation, and have accordingly lost your edge.

So if you're in a relationship and want to spot deception, ask a single, female (unbiased!) friend to help spot it for you. And if you're single but generally oblivious, pick your most self-aware friend for a second opinion. Evolutionary need has put these all-knowing tigresses atop the deception-detection food chain—they can help you ferret out a rat as opposed to being the tempting rat to a hungry ferret (unless you're into that sort of thing).

Put a hand on your widow's peak. About an inch below your fingertips in your medial prefrontal cortex is the home of your sense of self. Julian Keenan did a nifty trick: He used what is effectively an electric Ping-Pong paddle to zap this region in healthy subjects, overexciting every neuron within range, and thus for about a fifth of a second, knocking that one-cubic-centimeter area of the brain off the grid.

And while he did this, he flashed pictures of faces. Blasted subjects retained the ability to recognize faces of loved ones or even learned strangers, but for this fifth of a second, they failed to recognize themselves.

Interestingly, there's one type of person who retains sense of self even with the medial prefrontal cortex blasted: narcissists. Keenan explains that, "in narcissists, more brain areas are dedicated to self-deception." So when a narcissist's medial prefrontal cortex is taken offline, backup generators are in place to maintain that overblown sense of self.

It's a stark enough difference that soon there may be a neuroimaging diagnosis of narcissism. Does your sense of self sit in the medial prefrontal cortex box designed for it, or does it creep out to colonize other areas of your brain?

HOW TO SPOT A LIAR

Paul Ekman PSYCHOLOGY, UNIVERSITY OF CALIFORNIA–SAN FRANCISCO

Sure there are skin conductivity tests, pupil dilation tests, and now the burgeoning field of neuroimaging to test the truth of words. But unless you're packing a mobile lab, none of those do you a whole heck of a lotta good when asking your co-worker whether he dinged your door in the parking lot yesterday, a student if he plagiarized that essay, or your four-year-old if he knows anything about the toothpaste lining every tile crease in your bathroom. In those cases, you'll have to rely on lie detection the old-fashioned way: by the tingling of your own spidey senses.

Luckily these spidey senses can be trained.

"First, there's a simple rule to catching liars," says Paul Ekman, professor emeritus at University of California–San Francisco: "Things don't fit together. The voice doesn't fit with the content of words, the words don't fit with the look on the face, or the face doesn't fit with the words." This is the person who says "no" while nodding their head "yes," and simply knowing to watch for these incongruities can help you catch unpracticed liars.

But from there it gets trickier. "The second, more specific step is microexpressions," says Ekman. Rather than lasting two or three seconds, these expressions last about one twenty-fifth of a second and "almost always show emotions the person is trying to conceal," says Ekman. That is, if you can spot them. To these ends, Ekman's created a nifty online tool that trains your ability to recognize these microexpressions (www.paulekman.com, trial version free). In addition to being a nice training tool, it's fascinating to watch people flashing emotions that they almost instantaneously mask with more situationally appropriate expressions.

"But just because you detect a microexpression doesn't mean someone is lying," says Ekman. Imagine the police asked if you killed your spouse. You might flash a microexpression of anger at being questioned that has nothing to do with the truthfulness of your answers. Or if the police asked you about the quality of your marriage to the deceased spouse, you might flash sadness before going on to describe a happy marriage.

"When you see a microexpression, it's a cue to probe further," says Ekman.

Still, "there are about 5 percent of people we can't catch with this," says Ekman. He describes these 5 percent as natural performers. How can you learn the flip side of catching liars—how can you learn to be a liar yourself? Despite many requests for help in seeming more credible (mostly by politicians, both domestic and international), Ekman refuses to teach the strategies of good lying. "I only run a school for lie catchers, not liars," he says.

Paul Ekman has written books, including *Telling Lies*, is a frequent police trainer, and is scientific advisor to the show *Lie to Me*. His current research hopes to predict violent assaults ten to twenty seconds before they occur. He thinks he's about two-thirds of the way to an answer. "It'll at least allow you to duck," he says.

GROW HUGE CARNIVOROUS PLANTS

Louie Yang ECOLOGY, UNIVERSITY OF CALIFORNIA-DAVIS

You've seen the sign: BEWARE OF DOG! Yeah, that's badass and all. But imagine a yard full of giant humanivorous plants. That'd be totally boss!

And if homicidal plants are your game, then the person to talk to is Louie Yang, ecologist at the University of California–Davis. "There's a specific recipe for carnivorous plants," Yang says. "You need ample sunlight, ample water, but a lack of nutrients." This happens in rain forests, where the massive plant biomass sucks every last speck of nitrogen from the soil. And it happens in the high fens of the Sierra Mountains, where the boggy, sunbaked soil is nearly sterile.

In these nutrient-starved places, plants turn to the flesh of the living for food. Take, for example, the *Nepenthes rajah*, a pitcher plant common to the Borneo highlands. The *N. rajah* has sun and water aplenty, but its growth is limited by the nutrient-poor soil, and so it's evolved two foot-long traps with up to a gallon of digestive fluid, capable of trapping and eating creatures as large as mice.

A plant that eats small mammals rocks. But why stop there? Check this out:

When a pitcher plant catches a fly, it enlarges its fly-catching machinery. That makes evolutionary sense: Focus on what works. But when a plant starts focusing its resources on the creation of grabbing tools, its overall growth stalls—meaning it'll never get big enough to consume, say, your prying next-door neighbor. Or even her cat.

So, once you've got a budding Audrey II, resist your urge to keep feeding her flies. Instead, now's the time to start fertilizing her roots.

Yang caught wind of this trick when he noticed that the largest in a population of carnivorous plants was the one growing next to a pile of deer poop. Again, plants focus on what works: Nutrients entering through the roots signal the usefulness of a more extensive root system. More roots support a bigger plant. As long as the poop holds out the sucker will grow wide, strong, and large.

And this is cool: As a carnivorous plant starts to run out of nutrients, it'll shift resources back to fly catching.

So once you've fertilized your floral army to appropriately monstrous size, starve it to reprioritize growth of its prey-grabbing mechanisms. A hungry plant is a dangerous plant.

When I visited Louie Yang's lab at UC-Davis, he was contemplating a refrigerator that held ten thousand cigar-shaped insect traps and wondering how he might most efficiently go about slitting them open and examining the contents under a microscope to see what egg or larval goodies they held. I asked if maybe there were grad students or other proverbial "people for that"—leaving Yang and his oversized brain free to more efficiently design and manage investigations. But Yang echoed many scientists I talked with, saying that having his fingers in the grunt work of data collection is the way he gets ideas—he needs to slit insect traps to generate questions.

CHOOSE PEOPLE WHOSE COLLABORATION WILL BE GREATER THAN THE SUM OF THEIR PARTS

Brian Sauser SYSTEMS MANAGEMENT, STEVENS INSTITUTE OF TECHNOLOGY

"Look at cell phone cameras," says Brian Sauser, complex systems expert at Stevens Institute of Technology. "Originally they were designed to take pictures of your family. Now everyone's a reporter." From a somewhat mundane design purpose came a use that's fundamentally changed culture and society.

This is emergence: a behavior that arises spontaneously from a system. But just because any specific emergent behavior can only be reverse engineered and not forward engineered (you can tell how it came about, but couldn't have predicted it), systems designers remain able to put in place elements that maximize the likelihood of emergence.

In fact, according to Sauser, this idea of emergent purpose has become one of the central forces in twenty-first-century systems design. "It's been about control," he says, "but now we have to learn to build something and take our hands off the control." Look at the evolving use of micromessaging sites like Twitter. Or at the system of fiber-optic lines that carries the data of the Internet itself. From a flexible infrastructure come crowdsourced uses a designer may never imagine. Build it, open it up, and functionality will come—and in this brave new world, emergent functionality may far outstrip the usefulness of a designer's limited vision.

So how do you design a system with emergence in mind, be it a multicomponent technological marvel or simply a group of people working together on a project? How can you go about intentionally creating a system whose product exceeds your intention?

Sauser thinks of system design from the bottom up—as a combination of the basic building blocks of autonomy, belonging, connectivity, diversity, "and the interaction of the first four gives you emergence."

Unfortunately, there's frequently a trade-off, says Sauser. For example, systems of people tend to trade diversity for belonging (think of Salt Lake City). A similar trade-off can be true of connectivity and autonomy—once you streamline communication (connectivity) the temptation exists to use it for micromanagement, thus dooming autonomy.

But now imagine New York City. "At one level, it's extremely diverse," says Sauser. "You have Chinatown, Little Italy, etc." But on another level it's inclusive: "People came because by being different, they were normal." Sauser points to New York City as a rare example of a system with both high belonging and high diversity. Despite the individualistic spirit commonly held as essential to the New York mentality, "people walking down the street don't believe they're isolated," says Sauser. Instead, "People believe they're part of something bigger." Likewise, New Yorkers' high connectivity detracts little from their autonomy.

Certainly people in New York City could be more diverse, autonomous, connected, or belonging, but somehow this system has managed to push all four factors fairly high simultaneously. And this is why, according to Sauser, so much culture, innovation, and vision emerge from the city—outcomes for which you could never specifically design.

The same combination characterizes the best teams. To maximize the chance for emergence from a hypothetical group of people, "Think about the first four characteristics as win/win or win/lose," says Sauser. Try to increase each of these four factors without your group composition and protocols creating decreases elsewhere. For example, if you've brought diverse people together, you may need to train belonging. Or in a group with high autonomy, you may need to work to increase connectivity. Or in a team with massive belonging, you might need to ensure that team members remain able to work autonomously. You get the point.

You won't ever reach 100 percent in any factor, but by edging each higher without ceding the others, you can maximize the chance that the system you design will create emergent products that neither you nor any individual member could imagine.

Does diversity have inherent value? This may be the twenty-first century's most important question. Think ecosystems, think countries and immigration policies, think financial markets. Scott Page, professor of complex systems and political science at the University of Michigan–Ann Arbor and author of the book *Diversity and Complexity*, explored the question in the realm of problem solving. First, he and collaborator Lu Hong gathered a group of college students and tested them on a range of puzzles. Then they wondered: How would a team randomly chosen from this pool perform against a team of the top problem solvers? What they found is surprising—diverse teams outperformed homogenous teams of all-stars—but only if three conditions existed: (1) a baseline level of competence in all puzzlers (no total duds); (2) a wide enough range of puzzle types to nix the power of specialization (a complex system); and (3) a wide enough puzzler pool to ensure diversity is present.

Imagine a basketball team. "One power forward is great and two power forwards is good, but three is ridiculous," says Page. At a certain density of power forwards, you'll get every rebound but your homogeneity makes you susceptible to counter by one specific strategy: the full-court press. A team of power forwards would never get the ball up the floor.

In complex systems like basketball teams, "the hope is you create this interesting, innovative, pulsing, growing system," says Page. If your team does something noncomplex, like picking apples, you'd want a team of strong apple pickers. If your team's going to compete with Apple, Page shows that diversity for diversity's sake, as long as everyone reaches baseline competence, has value.

Do you concentrate best under pressure?

Do you contemplate best when melancholic? Are you most analytic when angry? A pair of studies shows it's best when mood matches the problem. Specifically, researchers at Northwestern University found that when they showed subjects a short comedy routine, amused subjects were then better at solving word puzzles with sudden insight. On the flip side, Dutch researchers showed that teams better solved analytic tasks when a certain degree of animosity existed in the room.

GET A JOB!

Roger Bohn MANAGEMENT, UNIVERSITY OF CALIFORNIA–SAN DIEGO

If you're a laid-off bum looking for work while living in a van down by the river, wouldn't it be great to know which field is poised for the kind of leap your skills could help create—aka, who'll hand over the $$ for work you're naturally inclined to do?

You've heard about evolution in industry—how today's techniques are built on yesterday's innovations—and it turns out there's a common progression of this evolution that allows you to predict, surf, and potentially profit from what's next in any field. "From semiconductor manufacturing to agriculture to aeronautics to firearms to professional services like architecture, all industries seem to fit a developmental model of six stages," says Roger Bohn, director of the Global Information Industry Center at the University of California–San Diego.

An industry starts as a craft, which you learn through experience or apprenticeship. "It's the 'lone gunman' or 'intrepid flier' stage," says Bohn. Picture a gent in a leather helmet and goggles peering over a precipice with a stick-and-skin glider strapped to his back.

Some of these people survive, and enter what Bohn calls "the rules-and-instruments stage." The effort becomes collaborative as the (lucky) intrepid flier adopts and installs others' innovations that allow him to fly in a more structured way. The Wright brothers took to the sky in 1903, but it was Paul Kollsman who added the accurate altimeter in 1928 and Jimmy Doolittle who showed pilots how to use the artificial horizon in 1932. As you'll note, both when you're going to hit the ground and at what angle you're likely to hit it are good things to know. "Before the artificial horizon, if you flew into a cloud, you were probably gonna die," says Bohn. This applied even to expert pilots—we use our inner ear to tell us which way is up, and in an airplane it doesn't work right.

The next stage, procedures, formalizes how you use all these multifarious gadgets. Aeronautics took this great leap forward in 1935 when the US Army Air Corps invented the preflight checklist. Today, before starting the engine on a tiny Cessna 140 you're required to check the tail wheel, flaps, fuel, seat belts, etc.

Next is automation—in aeronautics, this is the autopilot, or in the 1980 FAA training film *Airplane*, the copilot blow-up doll phonetically named Otto. In this stage, action takes place autonomously but with human supervision.

But in the final stage, computer integration, the human is pruned from the functioning system entirely. Machines are the overseers and humans are relegated to the job of technicians, troubleshooting any glitches that arise.

What creates industry evolution? Darwin would be happy to know it's natural selection, in this case taking the form of market pressure. It's bad for business when planes crash and it's also bad for business when you have to pay humans to do work that machines could do better (for the most part . . .). So generation II is necessarily more cost-efficient than generation I, and this drives all industries along the righteous sixfold path.

Some industries don't experience or are immune to these pressures and therefore fail to evolve. "Education hasn't made it far along the continuum," says Bohn. "Not enough economic pressure. [Or] take health care. What's happening today is that standard procedure is just fighting its way in."

If you need a job, your trick is this: First define the industry stage that matches your strengths. Are you an intrepid flier? A tinkering tweaker of existing systems? Are you a rule-maker at heart, salivating over the prospect of a seat-of-the-pants industry ripe for systematizing? Do you automate? Or are you a technician glitch-fixer?

Now find an industry that's in the stage that matches your specialty. For example, until the tech bubble popped in 2001, the Internet as a whole was the realm of intrepid fliers—now it's consolidating the best ideas.

Picking an industry that fits your fancy may be your best shot at getting out of the van down by the river.

In his book in progress, *From Art to Science in Manufacturing*, Roger Bohn writes about the two hundred years in which the Italian gun manufacturer Beretta went from individual craftsmanship to automated production lines, during which period craftsmen expertise was written into production protocol.

KNOW IF PEOPLE ARE OUT TO GET YOU

Jennifer Whitson MANAGEMENT, UNIVERSITY OF TEXAS MCCOMBS SCHOOL OF BUSINESS

A study, famous in circles in which this kind of thing is famous, showed pictures of pure static to falling skydivers (imagine the logistics). While plunging rapidly toward the unforgiving earth, skydivers were more likely than subjects sitting in the plane to see phantom pictures in the static.

Another study found that in periods of economic uncertainty, more books on astrology are published.

And another found that nursing-home patients who care for plants in their rooms have lower mortality rates than patients whose staff care for the plants.

What do these three findings have in common? Not yet! Keep reading.

Jennifer Whitson, professor of management at the University of Texas's McCombs School of Business, showed subjects a series of symbols and asked them to predict the next shape. Whitson then made half the subjects feel correct—revealing the shape they predicted—and made half the subjects feel incorrect, showing them an unrelated symbol (actually, there was no pattern, but that's beside the point). Then she showed subjects twenty-four images blurred by a snowstorm. The wrong-shape subjects found pictures in the snow, even when none existed.

Finally the punch line: it's all about control. Do you have it, do you lack it, and what will you do to get it. "Lacking control is a very aversive state," says Whitson. "People like it so little we'll do almost anything to take control." Like spotting patterns where none exist. Or reading astrology books.

Here's an example closer to home. Whitson presented subjects with the following story: You work in an office, monitoring and troubleshooting e-mail communications. You're up for a promotion. Suddenly you see a sharp rise in e-mail traffic between your boss and the person in the cube next to you. Then you don't get the promotion. Whitson asked, Are these two events connected? Subjects Whitson had primed to feel in control were likely to see a coincidence. Subjects whom Whitson had asked, prior to the story, to imagine a time in their lives in which they lacked control saw a conspiracy.

The person in the next-door cube is out to get you.

Or is he?

It's a tough call. And it's a call you shouldn't be making if you're out of control.

Whitson tells the following illustrative (and possibly apocryphal) story: Deep in winter, a group of Swedish soldiers goes on a military exercise. It starts snowing, and they get lost. Soon they start to panic—until one of the soldiers yells, "Wait, wait, I found a map!" which they follow back to base camp. When they get there, a superior looks at the map and says, "This is a map of a different mountain range!"

Every day, when trapped in your equivalent of a Swedish snowstorm (you'll know it when you see it), finding control—be it real or illusion!—can help you reclaim rationality in decision making. It's as if by retaking control of your mental space, you can be objective about the world at large. You can, as the saying goes, change the things you can change, and accept the things you can't—and you can know the difference between the two.

When the niggling worm of conspiracy whispers in your ear, Whitson recommends a quick mental check-in with an area of your life in which you do have control. Maybe keep pictures of your family on your desk. Or an assortment of flies from your last fishing trip. Not only can the feeling of control help you avoid the trap of the half-baked conspiracy theory, but, like Swedes in a snowstorm, confidence can lead to success.

When my kids were babies, I would lie in bed listening to the hum of a noise machine that I swear spoke to me. In my defense, it was on some sort of soundtrack loop so that "jungle" or "waterfall" or "summer night" settings did actually have audible patterns. I would start with a blank mind, eventually zero in on a layer of the innocuous pattern, it would suggest words, and the more I listened the more distinct the repeating words would become. I talked about this with my wife, a psychologist, which for reasons that should be obvious was a rather egregious mistake. I wonder: If I'd been able to take control of my sleep, my work, or my play at that point, would I have continued hearing words in the sound machine?

Whitson and collaborators explored the speech styles of young, dressed-down experts versus established, suited experts and found that experts are both more liked and more influential when their formal/informal speech style matches their appearance. If you're a young hotshot, speechifying just sounds pompous—even if you know your stuff. If you're a venerable lion or lioness, some degree of informality is fine, but can quickly be seen as crossing the line into inappropriateness.

DESIGN A POLL TO GET THE RESULTS YOU WANT

Charles Franklin POLITICAL SCIENCE,
UNIVERSITY OF WISCONSIN-MADISON

Your condo's front door faces the pool. In the summer months the irritation of noisy people splashing is balanced by the fact that you can so easily stroll across the walkway to join them. But this winter the condo association board has proposed a major pool renovation: months of jackhammering followed by the smell of sealant seeping into your living room and piles of construction materials outside your door.

Needless to say, you'd rather the pool renovation didn't go ahead as planned. Maybe if you can show that other owners are against it, you could stop it before it starts.

"Almost universally among real pollsters, there's no reason to bias the results," says Charles Franklin, poli-sci professor at the University of Wisconsin-Madison and codeveloper of pollster.com. This is because polls with fringe results receive fringe respect. But you're not a real pollster, and your results aren't likely to be set next to results from a half dozen other firms—you don't have to hit a sweet spot to be taken seriously. And luckily for you, there are many ways to sneakily insert poll bias, allowing you to fake a groundswell against pool renovations while continuing to appear impartial.

Franklin points first and most obviously to language. In the world of politics, Democrats may word an issue differently than Republicans (think "tax relief") and depending on the level of language bias, you see a similar bias in poll results. In your campaign against pool renovation, use the language of the faction that opposes it—listen to how your neighbors talk about the work and repurpose their language for your poll. Do detractors wonder about the wisdom of "ripping up the pool"?

The sequence of questions also matters. "Suppose a poll opens with a series of questions about the slow rate of change in unemployment, follows with the handling of the Gulf oil spill, then asks about Obama's job approval," says Franklin. The approval rate will rank lower than if the poll had opened with questions on issues that painted Obama in a more favorable light. At your condo, have there been memorable renovation fiascos? If so, highlight these fiascos in the way you ask about the pool.

Question sequence can also encourage poll respondents to frame issues in certain ways. If a political poll opens with questions about the economy, respondents are likely to evaluate later questions in terms of their economic impact, more so than if the poll had opened with questions about the environment. You can do the same: Ask how people feel about recent increases in condo dues before asking how they feel about pool renovations.

Still another way polls drift is the way they push for answers. "When you ask people factual information, women tend to score lower on knowledge than men, but it's largely due to answering 'don't know,' " says Franklin. "But if you push people to guess, it turns out that women are just as accurate." Men are simply more willing to guess up front. And so polls that push for answers tend to include in the mix a more accurate representation of the female vote. Is there a gender gap in pool opinion? If so, push or don't push for answers in order to exploit it.

Also, how deeply does a poll ask you to think about a question before responding? One theory of how we answer survey questions holds that we each carry one, true opinion—but it may take considerable digging to find it. And while digging we must pass and discard many opinions that are good enough. If a poll encourages you to satisfice, your quick answer can be much more beholden to poll mechanics, pop opinion, and the twelve-hour news cycle. So after inserting bias in your pool poll, asking for quick answers will dial up the effectiveness of this bias.

In fact, all this adds up to extreme difficulty for real pollsters to design a poll that doesn't do any of these things. For you, it means the pool renovation proposal days are numbered—as is any issue that provokes your shiny, new, deliciously nasty skills for showing that public opinion is on your side.

Early in the lead-up to the 2008 Iowa caucus, the American Research Group was the only firm in the state polling likely Democratic voters. Their polls showed John Edwards leading with Barack Obama far behind. Then, as things started to heat up in November and December, new pollsters arrived asking new questions, which showed very new results—suddenly Obama was polling much closer!

Was Obama really the beneficiary of a new popular groundswell, or did the change in polling methods more accurately describe the support that Obama had had all along? No matter, the media storyline read OBAMA GAINING SPEED IN IOWA! And this hopeful story line paved the way for Obama's sweep through later primaries and then the general election.

HOW TO BEAT SUCKERS AT POKER

Jonathan Schaeffer COMPUTER SCIENCE,
UNIVERSITY OF ALBERTA

Mathematician and computer games expert Jonathan Schaeffer at the University of Alberta solved checkers. After using up to two hundred computers running simultaneously for ten years to consider 10^{14} possible board states, his program, Chinook, eventually discovered a path of optimal play that never loses. And after solving checkers, Schaeffer turned his cerebral and computational firepower to another game—poker—specifically, two-player, limit Texas Hold 'Em.

In limit poker, you can only bet so much and so the game becomes a fairly mathematical exercise—based on your hole cards and the community cards, what's the chance of winning? (If this makes no sense, you can familiarize yourself with Texas Hold 'Em rules online.) Generally, if you have a more than 50 percent chance of winning, you bet.

But even this simple version of poker is tricky to study because "you can get lucky and unlucky and bad luck can last for a very long time," says Schaeffer. Bad luck can make even the best players look like rookies, so in a study it's hard to disentangle good play from good luck. Schaeffer and his research team found an interesting solution: They played two human-versus-computer pairs, each pair playing the same cards, but with the hands reversed. This way both sides get lucky or unlucky to the same degree. By comparing win/loss rates, Schaeffer and his collaborators discovered what strategies won over time.

"The best way to play against a computer is mathematically," says Schaeffer. Aggression or conservatism are trends that a computer will recognize and exploit.

"But playing against a human, aggression is correlated with success," says Schaeffer. "Pushing a lot of money into the pot forces your opponents to make many tricky decisions," and especially against weak opponents, these decisions are likely to result in mistakes.

When playing suckers, push chips.

In a surprisingly fun and interesting paper subtitled "Human Perfection at Checkers," Schaeffer tells the story of his program Chinook's 1994 battle against the human checkers champion, Marion Tinsley. In thirty-nine games, there were thirty-three draws, four wins for Tinsley, and two for Chinook. This was a great triumph for Chinook, considering that Tinsley only lost five other games between 1950 and his death in 1995 (paper linked from Schaeffer's faculty bio). What made Tinsley so great? According to Schaeffer, it was Tinsley's uncanny memory that even toward the end of his life allowed him to quote move sequences from games dating back to 1947, and a sixth sense born of experience. Yes, when playing checkers Tinsley "just knew" the best move—but, according to Schaeffer, it was because Tinsley had painstakingly added these moves to his mental Rolodex over many thousands of hours of play and study.

There are 43,252,003,274,489,856,000 possible states for a Rubik's Cube. Researchers at Kent State opened up a can of supercomputing whoopass on these states, showing that the max number of moves needed to solve the cube at any time is twenty. This task would've taken a desktop computer thirty-five years, but took supercomputers at Google about a week.

DISAPPOINTED OR PLEASANTLY SURPRISED? ADJUST YOUR EXPECTATIONS

Gordon Dahl ECONOMICS, UNIVERSITY OF CALIFORNIA–SAN DIEGO

What happens when you get a decent meal at a great restaurant? Or pay fourteen dollars to see an Oscar-winning film that turns out to be so-so? Or get a 3 percent raise when you expected 5 percent? You're disappointed, that's what. You expected greatness, you got mediocrity, and you're pissed. But look at it another way: Dude, you got a raise! That's awesome.

This is what economists call gain/loss reference dependence—human happiness really isn't about the amount of liquid in the glass, it's about that old half-full, half-empty thing. Or, more precisely, it's about how much liquid you expect to be in the glass. More than you expect and you're chuffed; less and you're disappointed.

How strong is the effect? It's hard to tell because it's extremely tricky to create emotionally charged expectations in the lab—a prerequisite to smashing these expectations and seeing how mad people get (or exceeding these expectations and looking for happiness).

So instead, Gordon Dahl, economist at the University of California–San Diego, turned to football. Before a game starts, there exists a very definite measure of expectations in the form of Vegas odds. You know who's supposed to win and by how much. And you know how emotionally charged a game is—is the team in playoff contention? Is the game against a traditional rival? Finally, there's an unfortunate but telling measure of how people are affected by football outcomes.

"We find that upset losses lead to a 10 percent increase in

domestic violence in the losing team's home city," says Dahl. If the losing team has an unusually high number of sacks and turnovers, make that a 15 percent spike. And if the upset loss is against a traditional rival, domestic violence in the team's home city increases by 20 percent. You can see it in police reports: As an upset starts to look likely in the game's final hour, domestic violence starts to climb, peaking just after the game, and returning to normal about two hours after the final whistle.

But it's not the loss that does it. If a team is expected to lose and then does . . . there's no spike. It's only when a team favored by four or more points chokes that football fans form fists. "The more salient the emotional shock is to you, the worse it is for your spouse," says Dahl.

And the rosy side isn't nearly as true. A home team's upset win does little to lower domestic violence. Or in other terms—sure, getting an unexpected great meal at a questionable restaurant makes you happy, but it doesn't nearly balance the unhappiness of a great restaurant missing. It's as if a happy surprise is (for example) +3 while a disappointment is -8. Over time, betting on restaurants is a losing proposition—this is likely one reason we get stuck in safe ruts, eating at the same decent place every time we go out. "But if we learned to manage our expectations, we'd all be better off," says Dahl.

You can't really adjust your surprise happiness/unhappiness payouts of +3/-8, but imagine lowering your expectations so that you're happily surprised at more than two-thirds of the new restaurants you visit. Now, in the long run, you're better off exploring.

Restaurants aren't the only medium in which expecting less allows life to frequently exceed your expectations. I grew up a Seattle sports fan and reflecting on how I now watch sports, even when the Mariners or Seahawks are ahead, I've ingrained the fatalistic attitude of "well, they'll probably blow it in the end."

My expectations stay low and so I'm happily surprised more than I'm disappointed (OK, with Seattle sports this barely allows me to break even).

The trick is to do this without becoming Eeyore. First, remember that your goal is to adjust your expectations without blunting your payoff. You can still root like heck, just imagine chopping a touchdown or three runs off Vegas's prediction for your team. And keep your lowered expectations to yourself—you don't want expecting less to lead to getting less.

Gordon Dahl also explored how violent blockbuster films affect violence in the neighborhoods surrounding theaters. Do violent films create violence? "Surprisingly," says Dahl, "during the movie, violent crime goes down." Dahl attributes this to temporary, voluntary incarceration: For the film's duration, violent people are off the streets. And the rate stays down for a couple hours after the film because after three hours in a theater, these violent people are sober.

GDP, per capita income, unemployment, educational performance: these are the measures of national well-being. But the United Kingdom hopes to add one more—a national happiness index. What's cool is that the prime minister imagines its use in driving and evaluating policy decisions. Just as an increase in GDP might be a reason for reform or an indication of an initiative's success or failure, so too could change in the happiness index drive decisions in government.

HOW TO CHANGE YOUR EVIL WAYS

B. J. Fogg PERSUASIVE TECHNOLOGY, STANFORD UNIVERSITY

"I eat a lot of popcorn," says B. J. Fogg, experimental psychologist and founder of the Persuasive Technology Lab at Stanford. "I cook it in oil and I eat it at night. It's a kind of addiction." But Fogg broke this addiction by announcing to his social network that for the rest of the month, he would become a popcorn teetotaler. This is self-manipulation—by putting his social reputation on the line, Fogg forced himself to change his snacking habits. And he makes a career out of designing technology that does the same to you.

"Can we be manipulated by robots and code into doing things we don't want to do? The answer is clearly yes," says Fogg. "But you can't just grab techniques from Alcoholics Anonymous and apply them to getting people to sign up for Flickr."

Instead, Fogg's Behavior Model (behaviormodel.org) lists three things that need to be true to change behavior: high motivation, high ability, and a trigger. Think about the person who bought this book. He/she must have wanted to buy it, had the ability to do so—money in the pocket, an Amazon.com account, etc.—and then something happened that actually made this person reach for his or her wallet. But exactly how to create these three things depends greatly on what kind of behavior you want to change.

Fogg's chart of fifteen types of behavior change (behaviorgrid .org) crosses five types—do a new behavior, do a familiar behavior, increase an existing behavior, decrease an existing behavior, and stop an existing behavior—with three durations: once, for a duration, and from now on. Fogg applies codes to each of the fifteen types of behavior change, like "BlueDot," which is performing a familiar behavior one time—for example, buying a book on Amazon.com. The type of change coded "BlackSpan" is stopping an existing behavior for a period of time—not eating popcorn for a month. "PurplePath" describes increasing a behavior from now on, like exercising more.

Fogg's Behavior Wizard (behaviorwizard.org) asks questions that help you define the code of the behavior you'd like to change, and then lands you in the appropriate resource guide. Simply click through the wizard for concrete, usable strategies.

For example, let's take a look at getting yourself or others to do a familiar behavior one time—a BlueDot behavior. If it ain't happening right now, ability, motivation, or trigger must be too low (or some combination thereof). Fogg recommends attacking triggers first—they're the easiest to manipulate and could be a quick fix. For example, if you want to make sure you go for a run this afternoon, schedule a text message for after work saying "Go for a run now!" If you want employees to do the ergonomic wrist stretches they've been taught, you can have a manager walk around and encourage an immediate two-minute time-out or send a quick e-mail memo.

If triggers don't do the trick, Fogg's next step is to adjust ability, which he divides into the categories time, money, physical effort, mental effort, social deviance (is the behavior unexpected?), and nonroutine (is it out of the ordinary?). For example, if customers are still not ordering movies online even after being bombarded by your e-mail spam campaign (in a benevolent way), perhaps you need to streamline the ordering process and thereby decrease the time or mental effort needed to make a purchase. Or perhaps even with a trigger to go running, you're stymied by the inability to find a matching pair of running socks. In this case, increase ability by sorting that pile of clean clothes.

Finally, and only finally, does Fogg recommend working with motivation. (To Fogg, going here first is the sure sign of an inexperienced designer.) This is because motivation's tricky to measure and tricky to adjust in a uniform way. For Fogg, putting his social network reputation on the line increased his motivation to abstain from popcorn. And maybe for you, imagining toned calf muscles would increase your motivation to run. But others might not care about their calves or mind backsliding on Facebook and may be more motivated to run by the thought of a healthier heart. So it's tricky. Fogg suggests thinking about motivation in terms of sensation (pleasure/pain), anticipation (hope/fear), and belonging (acceptance/rejection).

Fifteen types of behavior, three factors to create it, each with subclasses—Fogg boils it down to nine words, which he calls his mantra for behavior change: "Put hot triggers in the path of motivated people." Again, let BehaviorWizard.org be your guide. It will lead you sheeplike to a better tomorrow.

STOP YOUR BODY FROM DISSOLVING ITSELF

Gerald Weissmann MEDICINE, NYU SCHOOL OF MEDICINE

"The function of evolution is not to make it possible to drink martinis at my age. It's to get us to child-producing age," says Gerald Weissmann, professor emeritus at the NYU School of Medicine. A major way your body does this is by responding immediately and aggressively to infection.

"When microbes invade our tissue, throat, or gut, our cells produce hydrogen peroxide in defense," explains Weissmann. It's like the body's chemotherapy, killing the microbes, but at the cost of collateral damage in the surrounding tissue. This collateral damage is nothing compared to the havoc the microbes could otherwise wreak, and if you died at age forty as Nature intended, you wouldn't even notice it. But the degenerative effect of all this hydrogen peroxide adds up. Especially in those genetically predisposed, this tissue damage can result in arthritis and other autoimmune diseases.

But even when not fighting infection, the body produces hydrogen peroxide.

Your cells take in more oxygen than they really need. This makes sense—the body errs on the side of caution, and it's certainly better to have too much rather than too little oxygen. But excess has to be disposed of, which your cells do by combining excess oxygen with water to form H_2O_2.

Where does this hydrogen peroxide go? Over time, it accumulates in hair follicles, eventually poisoning away their ability to produce the coloring pigment melanin. This is why your hair goes gray. But, again, this should happen after you've reproduced, so evolutionarily speaking, who cares?

So the conclusion is obvious. If you want to avoid arthritis and gray hair, stop oxygen at its source: Don't breathe. But, as Weissmann points out, "This wouldn't work so well." Instead, you can try eating things that soak up this extra oxygen before it can become the corrosive fourth atom hooked onto a benevolent water molecule.

While, Weissmann says, it's extremely difficult to measure possible benefits of antioxidation from dietary supplements (how can you disentangle diet from all the other environmental and genetic factors?), he sees the most potential benefit in polyphenols such as those in most fruits (especially berries), most vegetables (especially ones you can imagine British people cooking, like cabbage), honey, and green tea. Weissmann specifically recommends resveratrol, which you might recognize as the wonder drug in red wine, and which Weissmann calls "my polyphenol of choice."

You've heard it before: red wine is good for your body. But did you know that it improves cognitive function, too? A seven-year study of 5,033 Norwegians found that moderate consumption of red wine (but not beer or spirits) improved cognitive function in both men and women.

SCAM-PROOF YOURSELF

Stephen Greenspan PSYCHOLOGY,
UNIVERSITY OF CONNECTICUT

I AM MARIAM ABACHA, WIDOW OF THE LATE NIGERIAN HEAD OF STATE, GEN. SANI ABACHA. How many words did it take—two? three?—before you knew this was spam? But once you get past desperately lame e-mails and people in trench coats selling "designer" watches, scams can get a little trickier, a little more borderline, and a little more appealing. Just ask Bernie Madoff's investors.

Or look at Vegas. Just after getting hitched, my wife and I found ourselves passing through Sin City as the cheapest way to visit West Coast schools, where she was looking at PhD programs. Being nearly indigent, we thought it'd be great to jump on a time-share tour, collect the free show tickets and meal vouchers, and use them to paint the town.

Fitting the classic profile of rubes, we were bussed out to a brand-spanking-new time-share high-rise, planted atop what was recently desert and would otherwise have been a strip mall. After an agent showed us around, we were placed in a holding tank and required to meet with a salesperson before we would be given our swag. Great—we were five minutes from show tickets and a free meal.

The salesperson asked us to estimate how many days we travel every year, and how much we spend on hotels while traveling, and explained that we could trade our weeks in Vegas for accommodations at any of their properties worldwide. Wow! It would take only twenty-five years to pay back our initial $80,000 investment, which, of course, would be doing nothing but gaining equity during this time. When we regretfully declined, the price went down to $40,000, and then eventually to $20,000.

And the thing is, it started to seem like a pretty good deal. Could we sleep on it? No. The offer was on the table—we had to decide now or never, and if "now," we could proceed directly to their financing center.

We chose "never." But it was much, much closer than it should've been. And I remember on the van ride back to the Strip, couples talked about how they'd done. The old hands had beat the system out of hundreds of dollars in casino chips in addition to the show and meal vouchers. And the few couples who'd become proud owners of a time-share in Vegas were just then realizing they'd been duped.

How, oh how, could they possibly have been so stupid?

"Think of gullibility as a threshold," says Stephen Greenspan, professor emeritus of psychology at the University of Connecticut and author of the book *The Annals of Gullibility*. Below this threshold you realize that with each "owner" paying $20,000 for ten days a year, that's a combined $730,000 for two rooms of slapdash construction in the desert. (Not to mention the fine print of astronomically high dues, blackout days, etc.) And above this threshold, well . . . you become an "owner." Greenspan lists four factors that push you toward this threshold: situation, cognition, personality, and affect. Ratchet them all high enough and anyone will tip into the abyss of foolishness. Learn to dial them down, and you can proof yourself against gullibility.

First, situation. This is a believable scam, or a "situation so compelling few people could resist," says Greenspan—like a time-share that takes only five years to pay for itself in reduced travel costs, which you can trade for travel anywhere in the world, and which you can sell at any time for more than you paid. That's believable, right? (OK, OK, I was young and foolish and in love!)

But if you have cognition—that is, background information and the mental firepower to use it—you still have hope of smelling the rat. I wish I could say that's how my wife and I snubbed the time-share scammers. However, I'm afraid I have to admit that we were just slightly out of their target demographic, having lied about our income to get the proffered free stuff. If we'd had the money, I'm not sure our cognition could have fended off the time-share. Certainly that was the case for many, many young couples that looked not so different from us.

Thirdly, woe be unto ye who are predisposed by personality to be unusually trusting. According to Greenspan, a trusting personality was a major factor in the success of a California scam targeting Mormons. The scammers, themselves posing as Mormons, promised to triple investors' money if they would contribute to a legal fund pushing for the sale of gold bullion from Israel to the Middle East. And these California Mormons were taken in, "in part due to their tendency to be trusting, especially of people in their religious community," explains Greenspan.

Finally, your affect matters. This is the in-the-moment version of personality and it's why there's free wine at art auctions. It's also why my wife and I weren't allowed to sleep on the rock-bottom offer of $20,000 for a Vegas time-share. "Gullibility happens under pressure, when you don't have time to think about things," says Greenspan, "and it helps explain why smart people do dumb things."

With the stamp of legal legitimacy, the Vegas time-share system had evolved to become nearly the perfect scam. You've got a believable situation, assault on cognition in the form of seemingly airtight logic to buy, the perfect rube personality in the demographics of the people they stick on the bus in the first place, and heightened affect through the pressure to buy it now or never.

But you, dear reader, are now armed with the tools to avoid the fate of so many rubes. You can't do much about the situation (that's up to the scammers), and it's tricky to alter your trusting personality, so focus on cognition and affect when making yourself scam-proof. First, you can be almost assured that any offer that's on the table now-or-never is something you'll wake up regretting. If you find yourself pressured to make a decision in the heat of the moment, always ask to sleep on it. Any legit offer will be there in the morning.

This also buys time to increase cognition. Try the phone-a-friend option. Outside the framework of the scammers' believable situation, does a trusted friend think it sounds like a good deal? And do your research—all it takes is a quick online search for "Vegas time-share scam" to return enough chatter to make even the most wide-eyed rube think twice.

So just chill out. Think. Do your homework. And you'll realize that the widow of the late Nigerian head of state is unlikely to transfer $20 million to your bank account, if only you pay the legal costs.

After I admitted to him how close I came to buying a sucker time-share, Greenspan told me the following story.

"When I was dating my now ex-wife, my mom called up and said that my aunt Ruby was selling her jewelry and she could get me a great deal on an engagement ring. I said I wasn't ready, but my mom pressed, and finally said she'd already bought the ring for me. My fatal mistake was saying 'Yeah, OK, fine,' and the next thing I knew I was getting congratulated on being engaged."

Greenspan's mother had duped him into marriage.

First, she created a believable situation—Aunt Ruby's jewelry—which Greenspan hadn't the cognitive background information or tenacity to fend off. And his personality was predisposed to trust his mother. And then his mom did something especially slick—when she said she'd already bought the ring, she ratcheted Greenspan's affect, requiring an immediate decision.

Greenspan cracked. And so would you.

AVOID BUYING STUFF YOU DON'T NEED

Brian Knutson NEUROSCIENCE, STANFORD UNIVERSITY

"On an airplane, you pick up SkyMall and you think Ooh, that's cool!" says Stanford neuroscientist Brian Knutson. "And then you look at the price and say No way!" In a nutshell, this is the theory of oh-wow/oh-yikes shopping (my words). Knutson can see it in the brain.

He had undergrads evaluate items in a catalog and, "Sure enough, when people saw products they liked, a reward area in their brain lit up," says Knutson. "Independently, a prefrontal area that monitors price lit up." Whichever of these two ignitions was the most powerful—"oh wow!" or "oh yikes!"—won the shopping battle.

The application on the marketing side is obvious: You could use fMRI imaging to perfectly price a product so that the reward for the target market is ever so slightly greater than the cost. People would buy and you'd make the max on each sale.

On the personal side, Knutson knows how to change these activation patterns. For example, beware the lure of bargains, which light your brain's reward pathways irrespective of whether the bargain price is actually low, allowing the reward area of your brain an extra bargaining chip to use against your stodgy prefrontal. But most important, Knutson found that paying with credit lit the nay-saying prefrontal less than paying the same amount with cash—"anesthetizing the money loss," he says.

If you want to dampen your shopping impulse, pay cash, not credit. And when you hit a bargain, allow your brain that extra second (or day) to think twice—reason overruling impulse—do you really need that battery-operated tie rack, even if it is 50 percent off?

Steve Schlozman, codirector of the Harvard Medical School psychiatry program says, "The balance between the frontal lobe's executive function and the amygdala's base instincts is what makes us human." And he offers imbalance as the cause of zombiism. In his decidedly tongue-in-cheek scenario, a decayed frontal lobe would leave no check for the anger and lust of the zombie amygdala. Schlozman also points out that the National Institutes of Health's definition of cerebellar degeneration describes a "wide-base, unsteady, lurching walk, often accompanied by a back and forth tremor in the trunk of the body." And degeneration of the hypothalamus can result in an insatiable hunger. In Schlozman's opinion, exactly this damage could be caused by a mutated influenza, which would be especially transmittable, say, by bite. The zombie tide is real, baby. And it's coming to get you. (For more science-of-the-undead fun, Google "Schlozman zombie podcast.")

Puzzle #9: Boomerang v. Zombie

Our hero throws a boomerang in the attempt to decapitate a zombie standing 30 yards away. But two seconds after he releases the 'rang, the zombie charges. The boomerang tracks a perfect circle at 30 mph, and the zombie instantly lurches to a surprisingly speedy 15 mph (no "Romero" zombie is this, apparently). Here's the question: Should our hero stand his ground and await the return of his weapon, or one second after the zombie charges, should he run at 10 mph toward a tree 8 yards directly behind him that would take him 2 seconds to climb to the height of safety?

CONTROL GOSSIP

Tim Hallett SOCIAL PSYCHOLOGY,
INDIANA UNIVERSITY-BLOOMINGTON

Gossip's bad, right? According to Tim Hallett, social psychologist at Indiana University, it depends on your point of view. "Gossip is a weapon of the weak," says Hallett. "Like the French Revolution, it's a way the powerless band together to retake power from authority."

In his study, the proletariat was composed of middle school teachers, and playing the part of a soon-to-be-noggin-challenged French noble was a new principal with an authoritarian administrative style and awkward social skills. Hallett videotaped these teachers as they went about their business—in conversations, in the teachers' lounge, and especially in teacher-led formal meetings—generating more than four hundred pages of single-spaced transcripts.

He coded the language of these transcripts and explored the data for insights into the inner workings of gossip.

One thing Hallett found is that "Gossip is a ubiquitous part of everyday life—it's unrealistic to ban it formally." If you're on the monarchy side of the revolution and thus have the goal of squishing gossip, banning it simply makes it more covert and potentially more insidious. Instead, providing a clear channel to voice discontent and clear mechanisms for getting things done in general removes the need for gossip to fill these roles. (Interestingly, elsewhere in this book economist Eli Berman recommends squishing terrorist organizations by increasing government social services, thus removing the population's need to turn to splinter groups for this help.)

Unfortunately, in the school Hallett studied, neither of these conditions was met and so gossip ran rampant. The task went from reducing its occurrence to "managing it informally by understanding how it works," says Hallett.

"First, the best thing to do is have lots of friends," he says. This seems obvious—if you're liked and respected, people are less likely to say bad things about you—but it also means that if gossip happens to turn against you, you're likely to have allies within earshot willing to deflect the damage. Assuming you or a friend is present, here's how to deflect the course of gossip.

In the early stages, Hallett found that gossipers were tentative, exploring the loyalties of the group in a way that allowed plausible deniability should a group member prove loyal to the monarchy. One way to do this is through sarcasm. "If the gossip gets back to the position of authority, sarcasm allows the gossiper to insist she was being literal, like 'I *said* you did a really good job!' "

Another obfuscation Hallett saw that attempted to infer bad things without saying them outright was something he called "praising the predecessor," as in a teacher describing conditions under the past administration as "so calm, and you could teach. There was no one constantly looking over your shoulder." What does this imply about the current administrator? This technique of praise as detraction works in any case of glaringly obvious comparison, as in a wife pointing out to her husband that her ex-boyfriend was such a good cook!

It's in this early evaluative stage that gossip can most easily be steered or diffused. To combat sarcasm or comparative praise, ask for clarification—force the gossiper to speak literally and thus take responsibility for the true meaning of the comments. Or try a preemptive positive evaluation—follow a loaded opening question (Did you see the boss's new shoes?) with abject praise (Yeah—Velcro's back, baby!). If all else fails, switch the gossip to an innocuous target (Dude, that was nothing—did you see the shoes on Steve from accounting?).

Nipping detrimental gossip adroitly in its early stages—before gossipers discover everyone's loyalties—can allow you to save the target of gossip without putting your head alongside his or hers on the chopping block of the resistance.

In another study, Hallett found a positive feedback loop for the spread of emotion through a workplace–if a person naturally or intentionally starts broadcasting an emotion, it not only spreads by interaction, but as it spreads the original emotion also amplifies. This, of course, causes more spreading and more amplification until the emotion, in Hallett's words, "blows up."

Puzzle #10: The Gossip Web

Did you hear that Annabel and Mark told everybody they'd baked the cupcakes for the party, but actually bought them at the bakery in the next town over? Can you guide the important message through the social network on page 141? The message can only travel between touching boxes (no diagonals), and must be brought into any next box by someone in the first. For example, to get from the starting box to the one below it, you could go guy-with-glasses to guy-with-glasses. Then continuing down the column, you could go top-hat to top-hat.

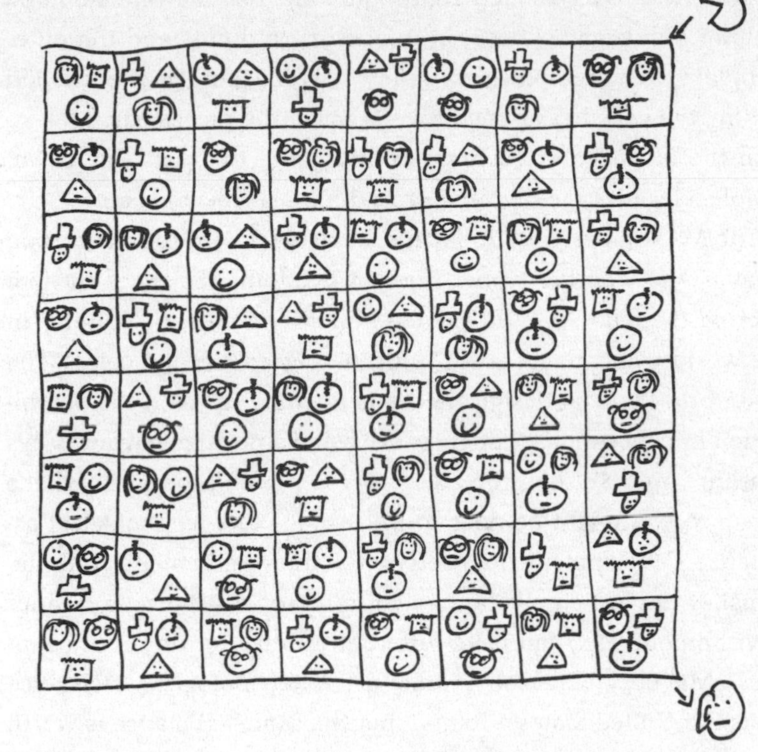

DO THE UTILITY SHUFFLE TO DIVIDE CAKE, CHORES, CARBON, AND THE BILL

Eric Maskin ECONOMICS, INSTITUTE FOR ADVANCED STUDY

"Parents want both kids to be happy with the piece of cake they get," says Eric Maskin, economist at Princeton's Institute for Advanced Study. A parent can do his or her best to cut the cake evenly, but the problem is, "the kids themselves might not see this as an equal split," he says. In addition to the perception of size inequality, maybe only one piece has a sugar Batman, or maybe one is slightly more endowed with frosting. These things may matter more than you could possibly imagine—they may have different "utilities" to different kids. So parents of kids who have reached sharp-knife age use the time-honored trick of divide-and-choose, in which one kid cuts and the other kid picks. "The reason this works," says Maskin, "is that the kid cutting the cake has an incentive to make the pieces equal."

In the language of economists and game theorists this clean, simple, elegant cake-dividing procedure is a "mechanism."

Eric Maskin designs similar mechanisms for things like carbon treaties—he won the Nobel Prize in Economic Sciences for pioneering the field—only in the case of carbon cuts, no country in the world wants to get stuck with the bigger piece of cake. "The goal of mechanism design theory is to come up with the combination of concessions that gives everyone a positive payout," says Maskin. And just like the cake, this is possible because what's cheap to you might be dear to me—things like technological assistance, development aid, preferential trade agreements, international or domestic political capital, military assistance, a cleaner environment, etc., can have different utilities for different countries. Maybe giving some amount of technological assistance costs the United States 4 "chits," but the same assistance is worth 8 chits to Brazil. An efficient treaty would ask Brazil to pay for this assistance with 7.99 chits of carbon reductions, which might be worth more to the United States in political capital than the 4 chits of tech assistance it paid. Because both countries come out ahead, both would sign the treaty. And then we would all stand arm in arm atop a hill drinking Coca-Cola and singing.

This idea of personal, differing utility allows you to amiably divide many things. Think about splitting up household chores—maybe you'd do the dishes and the laundry if your spouse will set a mousetrap in the garage. Or imagine dividing a Sunday's worth of free time—is it worth six hours of strolling hand in hand on the beach for two hours of uninterrupted viewing of the Chelsea v. Manchester United game?

The variable utility of cutting cake and carbon also allows you to split the restaurant bill with a group of friends. It's not fair to split the bill evenly—you're not going to freeload lobster when all I got was a grilled cheese sandwich! (This is the venerable problem called "the diner's dilemma," but that's another long story.)

So imagine you're not splitting the bill evenly. Who should pay a bit more and who should be silently allowed to pay a bit less? Well, what's an extra $10.00 actually worth to you in terms of utility? Like cutting carbon, what somewhat intangible concessions might you get for paying extra? Might you gain the equivalent of $10.01 in goodwill? (The same amount of goodwill might only have $1.50 in utility to your cash-strapped high school buddy who still lives at home.) Does withholding $10.00 from the pot actually cost you $10.01 in the utility of reduced sex appeal due to looking like a cheapskate?

A good mechanism is efficient—everyone maximizes his or her personal utility by giving up what's cheap to gain what's dear, thus coming out ahead on aggregate. It might only take a little tricky utility shuffling to make a good deal all around. And at the very least, next time you get stuck paying the extra ten bucks on the tab, you'll be aware that you got something for it.

Puzzle #11: Cake Cutting

For whatever reason, you've chosen DIY cake cutting over allowing your two kids to divide-and-choose. Now the problem is how to divide the cake evenly. Imagine the small pan is a perfect 10 × 8-inch rectangle, 2 inches deep. On one side sits an undividable sugar Batman, worth exactly 27 in^3 of cake to kid A and 8 in^3 to kid B. But it's kid B's birthday and so both see it as fair if kid B's piece is 1.5 times as big as kid A's. (What? Isn't this how it works in your family?) Who should get the sugar Batman, and how much cake should each kid get?

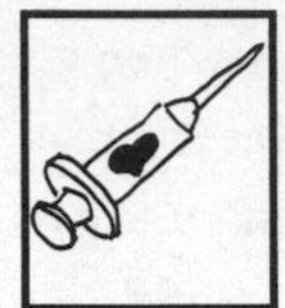

MIGHT AS WELL FACE IT: ADDICTED TO LOVE

Larry Young NEUROSCIENCE, YERKES NATIONAL PRIMATE RESEARCH CENTER

"Drugs hijack the circuitry that evolved for things like love," says Larry Young, neuroscientist at Yerkes National Primate Research Center. Most recreational drugs create dopamine release in the brain—thus our drug-induced sense of exhilaration and euphoria. And it's dopamine that's produced when you first fall in love. In the brain, the early stages of a relationship are very much like snorting cocaine.

And in many animals with one-and-done mating, that's where the molecules of love end. It's pleasurable, it's exhilarating, then it's done and the animal is croaking, dancing, or butting heads in search of the next rush.

But not in prairie voles.

"In prairie voles, we see three molecules involved in mating," says Young. First, of course, is dopamine. But female voles add oxytocin to the mix. "Mothers release it during labor and when nursing," says Young, "and when a female vole is being mated by a male, she releases oxytocin in the brain." Male voles release vasopressin, which is only a couple amino acids different from oxytocin, and in other species is involved with territorial behavior.

What does this overlay of oxytocin or vasopressin do? "We can inject female brains with oxytocin or male brains with vasopressin and voles will bond without mating," says Young.

Does this imply that the human experience of love could be chemical?

Young points to a Swedish study of one thousand couples that charted which men were well endowed in something called the microsatellite polymorphism in the brain's vasopressin receptors (don't worry, you won't be tested on that), and asked the couples questions about their relationships. Men who were biologically doomed to trap less vasopressin were twice as likely to report a crisis in their marriage in the past year, twice as likely to be unmarried but shacking up with a partner, and much more likely to report dissatisfaction with their relationship. In short, less vasopressin made males bond poorly.

Similarly, Young points to many studies that have confirmed the bonding properties of oxytocin, finding that it "increases eye-to-eye contact, increases ability to read emotions of other people, it increases empathy—also one study showed that if you gave oxytocin to a couple that was having a conflict, after the conflict they would have fewer bad emotions."

And so love is chemical.

But user beware: This neurochemical cocktail of love is addictive. "Love goes from lots of dopamine to a later phase which is basically togetherness to stop withdrawal symptoms," says Young. And once the dopamine is gone, there had better be enough vasopressin (men) or oxytocin (women) to make it in both partners' best interest to refrain from looking for a new source of dopamine outside the relationship.

So as new love gives way to the routine of sex every other Wednesday after *Dancing with the Stars*, dopamine cedes to vasopressin/oxytocin. But what happens when love is removed altogether? What happens when you split with a partner? "If a vole loses its partner, it shows symptoms of depression similar to withdrawal," Young says. "What does the animal do? It goes to seek a new partner."

This is the rodent equivalent of a rebound relationship. Rather than pushing through the depression of withdrawal that eventually allows your brain chemistry to return to prerelationship levels, it's much, much easier to find pleasure in a new drug, even when this new drug is a detrimental source of dopamine.

Instead of rebounding into whatever gives you a quick fix, give your brain chemistry a break. After an ending, take the time you need to reset your head before another beginning.

The news flash in a study from Mount Sinai School of Medicine is that both good and bad memories of Mom were strengthened with a dose of good old oxytocin. After a whiff, securely attached men remembered Mom more fondly, and insecurely attached men remembered Mom even less fondly. It may be that oxytocin doesn't simply increase attachment, but that it adds saliency to emotional memory of any sort.

CREATE FALSE MEMORIES TO GET MORE PEACH SCHNAPPS

Elizabeth Loftus PSYCHOLOGY,
UNIVERSITY OF CALIFORNIA-IRVINE

My earliest memory is of living in Bergen, Norway, when I was two. I vividly remember looking out at fjords from a ferryboat, and there's a picture of me standing next to a troll statue holding up two fingers and smiling. I've heard my parents talk fondly about Bergen. But the thing is, I recently found out my parents lived there before I was born. The picture in question was taken during a visit to the Tyrolean kitsch town of Leavenworth, Washington, and my vivid memory of fjords and ferries must be tangled with a trip to or from Bainbridge Island. It turns out that without meaning to, my parents planted within me a false memory.

Elizabeth Loftus knows how to do it on purpose.

First, she gathers information. "We learn about a subject's personality, about thoughts, about different foods, all to give what happens later some credibility," says Loftus, a psychologist at the University of California–Irvine and pioneer in the study of memory.

Then, (for example, in one series of studies) Loftus tells a subject that the research team fed the subject's information into a supercomputer that knows, based on this information, what happened to the subject as a child. The computer lists many of the subject's real experiences and intermixes one false experience—in the case of these studies, suggesting the "memory" of getting sick from dill pickles, hard-boiled eggs, or another food. Loftus then asks the subject to talk about these experiences. Eventually, many subjects will adopt the false memory, filling in details about the childhood food illness.

But how can you tell the subject has actually adopted the memory, rather than simply being agreeable by paying lip service to researchers' suggestions?

"After I seduce you into believing that you got sick from a food as a child, you'll avoid the food now," says Loftus, who watched subjects' food preferences after the memory insertion. Simply, the false memory of barfing pickles becomes embedded to the point that without further prompting, subjects avoid pickles in the postinterview buffet.

In addition to its implications for investigations, psychologists' couches, and courtrooms, the ease of false memory insertion should allow you to mind-punk your friends into giving up their share of the peach schnapps (my college friends will get this inside joke, which unfortunately requires no false memory). Start a week earlier with the story, "Dude, do you remember the time when . . ." and when your target denies it, counter with, "Well, of course you wouldn't remember it, but it was pretty gnarly. . . ." Once your target's accepted the truth of his past transgressions, you can safely pass around the schnapps, confident you'll get your fair share.

SAVE THE WORLD IN YOUR SPARE TIME

Luis von Ahn COMPUTER SCIENCE, CARNEGIE MELLON UNIVERSITY

The idea is not a new one: All those people pedaling away in spinning class, going nowhere, burning calories to push against the adjustable friction of their back wheels. Shouldn't we, like, use that energy for something? Couldn't we power the lights in the gym, or heat the sauna, or digitize ancient manuscripts?

The good news is we're already doing the last one, thanks to Luis von Ahn. But the extra power he harnesses isn't calories from quadriceps, it's the computational power of millions of brains. It started with another of his projects, the Captcha. That's right, Luis von Ahn, MacArthur fellow and computer scientist at Carnegie Mellon University, is the guy (along with Manuel Blum) who developed the little text box gatekeepers that you squint at whenever you sign up for a new online service or post a link to a message board—it's the way computers can tell you're you, or at least human. "They're pretty annoying," says von Ahn, "and worldwide they waste about five hundred thousand hours a day." Von Ahn started wondering if, like powering the lights by pedal, he could put these half-million hours a day of cerebral busywork to better use.

And here's the thing about a Captcha: By design, it asks you to do something a computer can't, that is, translate a visual image of a distorted word into text. "Your brain is doing something amazing," says von Ahn.

Enter the Google Books Library Project. Ancient manuscripts are rotting, and before they go the way of *Tony Orlando and Dawn's Greatest Hits* (which died with the 8-track never to boogie again) Google hopes to digitize them. So there are people in libraries around the world scanning these decaying pages by hand. The scanned images are then fed into text recognition software, which translates the images into text files.

Trouble is, even the best OCR software isn't perfect, and in manuscripts more than one hundred years old OCR has an error rate more than 30 percent.

So instead of simply digitizing books as best they can and settling for Shakespeare's "To be ornut Tope, thatis the truncheon," the Google Books Library Project feeds each scan into two different text recognition softwares, and when the software disagrees on a word, they call in an impartial, third-party arbiter: you. The software snips the image of the word in question and places it in a Captcha box (now called reCaptcha), and you play the part of translator. Whenever you type the words you see in a reCaptcha box, you're translating a word from an ancient manuscript or from the *New York Times* archives or from any number of previously undigitizable text sources that would otherwise eventually fade into the great circular file of cultural forgetting.

This is why there are two words in a reCaptcha box—one against which the computer checks you, and one the computer doesn't know, that you translate. Your opinion is compared to other users' opinions until a word gets 2.5 consistent "votes" (humans are worth one vote, the OCR software is worth one-half), at which point it's considered solved. Easy words, on which all humans agree, are recycled to become the control words against which the computer measures your humanity.

"We're doing 70 million words a day," says von Ahn, "a couple million books a year; and there are 750 million distinct people who have digitized at least one word." That's one out of every nine people on earth who's helped turn decaying images of ink on paper into everlasting ones and zeros.

"Humanity's greatest achievements—the pyramids of Egypt, the Great Wall of China, the Panama Canal—were all done with, like, 100,000 people," says von Ahn. In his opinion, this was due to the impossibility of coordinating more than this 100,000. And so there was a cap on potential human achievement. "But now with the Internet, we can coordinate 100 million. If 100,000 people could put a man on the moon, what could we do with 100 million?"

Researchers in the new field of "culturenomics" are mining the 5,195,769-and-growing volumes of the Google Books Library Project for elements of cultural change. For example, you can see the suppression of the Jewish artist Marc Chagall in Germany as the difference in the frequency of his name in English and German books. In English, Chagall continues to rise through the Nazi period, whereas in Germany, there's a sharp drop-off in the printing of his name. And, interestingly, Darwin took off during and just after his lifetime, but it wasn't until the discovery of the structure of DNA that his name exploded into the cultural lexicon.

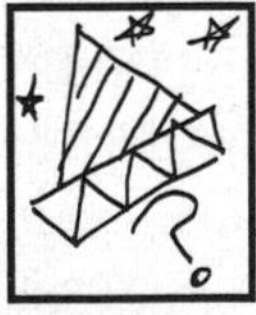

USE FACEBOOK TO PICK YOUR PARTY POSSE

Robin Dunbar ANTHROPOLOGY, OXFORD UNIVERSITY

Admit it: You'd love to—just once!—do a karaoke version of "Pinball Wizard" while standing on a bar in a sequined cape, codpiece, and oversized sunglasses.

Or is that just me? Anyway. . . . you can't. That's because

it's no fun to party alone, and the 150 people you know would excommunicate you for the "Pinball" incident. In fact, Robin Dunbar, director of the Institute for Cognitive and Evolutionary Anthropology at Oxford University, has shown that people in societies around the world tend toward this magic number of 150 as what he calls "the cognitive limit to the number of individuals with whom any single person can maintain stable relationships." It's true in Tennessee, it's true in South Africa, and it's also true on Facebook. "Actually the average number of Facebook friends is between 120 and 130," says Dunbar, "perhaps because the other 20 or so people include Granny and the like, who aren't online."

So your goal is this: to act depraved while minimizing the damage to your 150-person network. The key is to pick just the right friends to party with. "In dense networks, people police the community," says Dunbar. You see this in the Amish or Hutterites. "If you do something offensive, you offend everyone in your community and become a social outcast." But Dunbar can show a developing trend toward more splintered networks. "Now, it may be that you're born in San Francisco, go to school in New York, and get a job in Florida," he says, meaning that your network is fragmented into perhaps five independent fingers of thirty people each. If you party with just the right, small splinter, the rest of your network need never know.

The trick is remaining hyperaware that whomever you party with will post pictures of you in a codpiece back to their own Facebook accounts, which will then be seen by all their friends. Are there people in your small, potential party splinter who are members of multiple lists? For example, is one of your college friends also on your list of current work buddies? If so, you may not be able to party with college friends for fear of your behavior leaking between groups and generally going viral through your 150-person network.

Rewrite your friends lists as a Venn diagram as shown below.

Now look for circles with the least (or no) overlap. If your friend circles are unusually dense, with unavoidable overlap—more Hutterite than modern American—look for the overlap with the shortest reach.

Now read this book's entry about identity economics to discover how much your depraved behavior is likely to cost you in any given splinter (acting contrary to your expected identity carries a cost in "personal utility"—and you may have different identities in different splinter groups). Imagine the identity cost in any group multiplied by the number of people in the group. How much does your desired brand of depravity cost you?

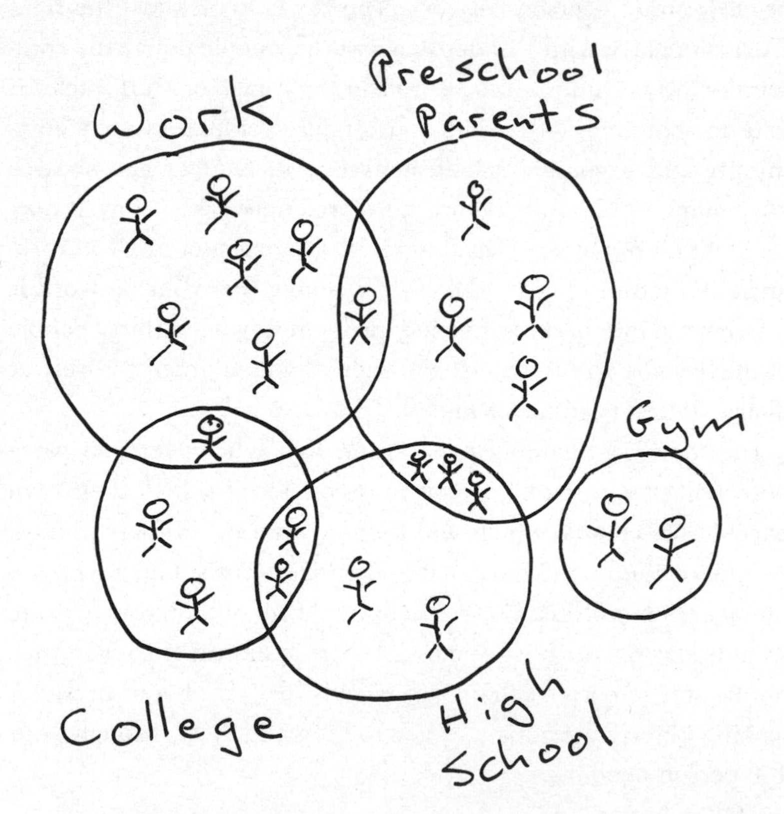

The splinter with the least cost, gentle reader, is the group with which you should sing "Pinball Wizard."

Dunbar's recent work finds that people with large social networks have distinctly looser emotional ties to most members. And so it's as if, instead of being bound by the number 150, the size of a social network is bound by a finite amount of emotional energy, which a person can choose to distribute as they see fit.

Puzzle #12: Friends Add Up

You have friends from grade school, high school, summer camp, college, your first job, grad school, your kids' friends' parents, an online fantasy football league, and your current job. If friend groups can only be composed of 13, 15, 17, or 32 individuals and each subsequent friend group (in listed order) has equal to or greater than the number of friends as the previous group, how many friends does each group have in order for your total number of friends to be exactly 150?

"There's this old question in sociology asking why your opinions and interests are similar to those of your friends," says MacArthur genius and Cornell computer scientist John Kleinberg. "Do your friends influence you to become more like them, or do you seek out like-minded friends?" Kleinberg answered this question using Wikipedia, where you can quantifiably see that people who talk have similar editing behavior. Great, you're like your friends. Only, by downloading the multiterabyte file that holds all of Wikipedia's history, Kleinberg was able to ask if "similarity in editing behavior started before or after people started talking to each other." What you see is this: "As people get closer to each other in the network, their editing behaviors become much more similar," says Kleinberg, "but after they meet, their editing becomes only marginally more similar." So the answer to sociology's question is this: You seek out like-minded friends.

HOW TO GET AWAY WITH A CRIME IN BROAD DAYLIGHT

Daniel Simons and Christopher Chabris PSYCHOLOGY, UNIVERSITY OF ILLINOIS-URBANA-CHAMPAIGN, UNION COLLEGE

In a recent fit of optimism, I joined a gym. And the day I signed up, I noticed a police officer poking around the gym lobby. When I asked the membership agent about it, he told me that the day before, someone had stolen a spinning bike (like the life-sucking machine in *The Princess Bride*). It had been there at the 5:30 p.m. class, but was gone at the 7:00 p.m. class. There's only one exit that doesn't set off a fire alarm, and the exit leads through a crowded gym, down the stairs, and past the staffed front desk.

In other words, someone had walked out the door with a one-hundred-pound bike in plain view of at least ten and likely fifty people. Maybe it was under a huge tarp or something, but still . . . don't you think you would've noticed?

Maybe, maybe not. Check this out.

While both at Harvard, psychologists Dan Simons (now at the University of Illinois) and Christopher Chabris (Union College) filmed six people passing a basketball. Three wore white shirts and three wore black shirts. In the video they jump around while inexpertly bouncing and tossing the ball from one person to the next. Simons and Chabris showed subjects this film and asked them to count the number of passes by one or the other team. After the film they asked subjects if, just maybe, they noticed anything strange or unexpected during the film.

Half didn't.

This, despite the fact that a woman in a gorilla suit walks obviously into the center of the group, stops to look at the camera, and thumps her chest before continuing off screen.

Again, people failed to notice a lady in a fricking gorilla suit. You can find the video online by searching for "invisible gorilla," which is also the title of the duo's very well written, thoroughly researched, and entertaining book.

First, this is potentially the coolest experimental design ever. Second, again—Dude, a gorilla suit! Come on!

But the experiment isn't a one-hit wonder of coolness. Simons and another collaborator—Daniel Levin—ran a study that starts with a researcher stopping a stranger to ask directions. Great. Then two people carrying a large door walk through the middle of their conversation. And during the short time of obfuscation, the researcher grabs the door and one of the carriers takes his place. When the door passes, this new person picks up the conversation where it left off.

Imagine the mind trip: You're talking to someone who magically and immediately morphs into an entirely new person. It's enough to make you infarct something. That is, assuming you notice at all. Again, as you can see with a quick online video search, half of us don't.

Granted, these two studies are different—the first explores selective attention, and the second explores change blindness—but they both nicely demonstrate that people can be massively oblivious to even the patently obvious.

So it's very possible to carry a spinning bike through a crowded gym without anyone's noticing. Note this is very different from people's noticing and not intervening—that jumps into the realm of bystander apathy, with the decision to help or not help a victim depending on behavioral economic payoffs like risk, reward, and relatedness (see this book's entry on altruism). No, here we're dealing with another thing entirely: The bystanders are completely unaware of the crime.

So . . . how might you take advantage of this phenomenon?

In a nice twist on the original gorilla experiment (for which the good doctors received an Ig Noble Prize), Simons and Chabris asked subjects not only to count the number of passes on one team or the other, but to keep track of the number that were bounce passes or chest passes. "With a higher cognitive load, people notice the gorilla even less," says Chabris.

Simons explains, "We have a limited pool of attention. If you're paying a lot of attention to something, you have less attention available to spend on noticing other things. This helps us focus on important things while filtering out distractions. One consequence of filtering out distractions, though, is that we sometimes filter out things that we might want to see."

Like a lady in gorilla suit. Or the fact that your conversation partner has shape-shifted. Or someone lugging a spinning bike past the gym's front desk.

So if you're trying to do the lugging, do it among people whose brains are otherwise occupied. During the Final Jeopardy round is ideal. If not, the age-old technique of an accomplice creating a distraction is a good one—and it doesn't even need to pull attention away from your physical space as long as it takes up bystanders' mental space. Perhaps your accomplice can aggressively shout brain teasers?

Also, "if a bank robber has a gun, bystanders are less likely to remember his face," says Simons. Paying well-deserved attention to the gun detracts from the attention available for face recognition. This is similar to the theory of garish invisibility employed by Bill Murray in the underappreciated 1990 movie *Quick Change*, in which Murray flamboyantly navigates an airport in a clown suit while escaping after robbing a bank. While not exactly lab conditions, it's as if people see the clown suit and not the wearer.

As for the exercise bike, I'm sorry to report the mystery was never solved.

Simons and Chabris also happen to be freakishly good at chess. (Chabris has been a chess master since 1986, was editor of *Chess Horizons*, and founded the *American Chess Journal*.) Chess is a fertile ground for researchers because there are rankings—you know quantitatively how good people are. And Chabris and Simons used this data to find something cool: Players with lower rankings massively overestimated how good they were, while players with higher rankings were much closer in their estimations of their skill. (See this book's entry with David Dunning.)

THE SHORTEST PATH BETWEEN ERRANDS

William Cook MATHEMATICS, GEORGIA INSTITUTE OF TECHNOLOGY

OK, here's the situation: In the short time your kids are at preschool, you have to deposit a check, buy organic gummy vitamins with iron at the hippie grocery co-op, buy Drano at the nonhippie supermart (while avoiding eye contact with anyone you might've seen at the first), pick up dog food, drop off overdue books at the library, and get a bike tire repaired.

Six errands flung to the far corners of town, with a web of connecting roads and a ticking clock. Do you hear the *Mission Impossible* theme music? Go!

Oh, I forgot the added bonus: If you figure out how to find the shortest route, the Clay Mathematics Institute will give you a million dollars. That's because, to date, no one has provided a general solution (or proven a solution's impossible) to this type of problem—called "the traveling salesman"—in which you have to minimize total distance traveled among many points.

It has many applications: Imagine you're standing in the middle of a court littered with tennis balls. What's the shortest distance you can walk to pick them all up? Or how can you see all the major landmarks of Paris in an afternoon?

The problem is that, "as the number of stops grows toward infinity, so too does the number of possible routes," says William Cook, mathematician at Georgia Tech. At some point, the magnitude of possible choices simply overpowers computational resources. So Cook takes a novel approach. Instead of using brute force computation to search through the haystack of nearing-infinite routes for the best solution, Cook explores sufficing—how can you *nearly* find the shortest tour between errands, and once you have a candidate, how can you know how good or not good it is? Cook says, "If I give you a ten-mile tour, you might be unsatisfied, unless I can guarantee with some degree of certainty that there are no shorter tours."

This allows us to start our errands without having to wait the many generations the Deep Thought supercomputer might take to discover the optimal route of forty-two miles (and if you get this reference, I imagine you'll find many little chuckles throughout this book).

So how should you suffice? "If every time you go to the nearest place you haven't yet visited, it gets you within 25 percent of the shortest tour," says Cook. What errand is closest to you? Go there. And then look around again—now which one's closest? Continue until you've visited each stop, and you're mathematically certain to be within 25 percent of the shortest route. (Remember to think time and not distance when computing "nearest.")

Once you're cool with that, here's a nice refinement: Draw your tour, always going to the closest place not yet visited, and then look for places where the route intersects itself. Uncross any crosses. (This makes no sense until you draw it, like on the next page, and then it's obvious). This gets you within 10 percent of the optimal tour. If you can solve the tour completely, the Clay Institute has a million bucks for you.

The traveling salesman problem is a clean illustration of applied versus pure mathematics. Cook has solved optimal tours up to 33,810 stops and tours within 1 percent of optimal are available for millions of stops. But that's not a solution. To date, there exists no general procedure for finding the optimal route among X number of stops.

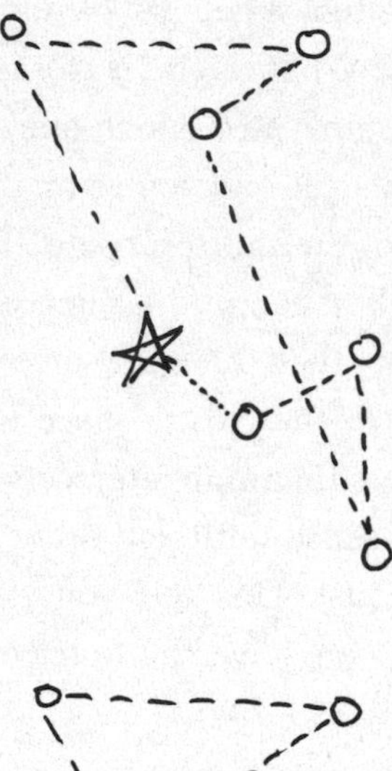

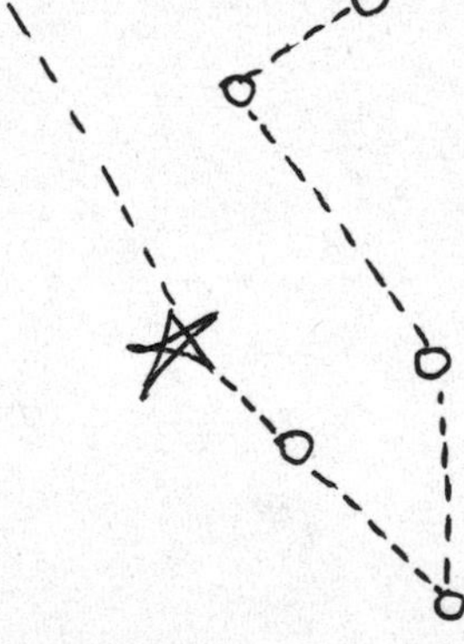

Puzzle #13: A Three-Hour Tour?

Draw the shortest tour starting and ending at the house, and touching all the points in the picture below.

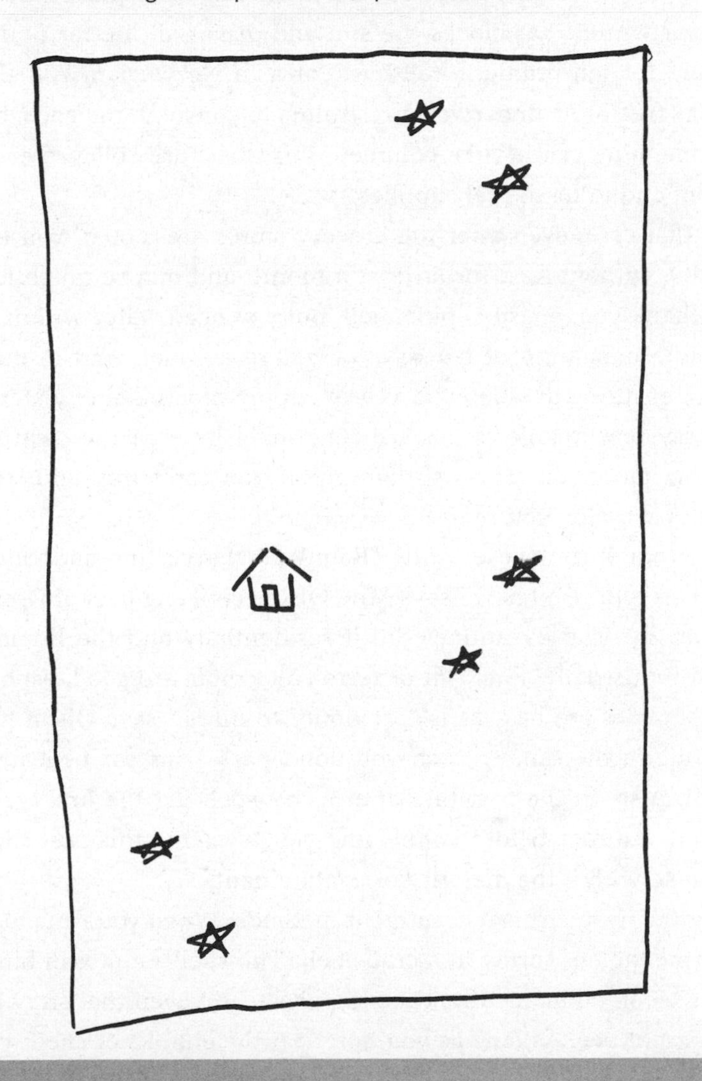

HOW TO SURVIVE ARMAGEDDON

Mira Olson CIVIL ENGINEERING, DREXEL UNIVERSITY

Let's imagine Armageddon comes not in the form of a mighty asteroid that obliterates the planet, or as nuclear winter that blocks the sun and drives all life far underground for ten uranium half-lives, or as a Norwegian wolf that breaks free of its underworld restraints to consume the gods, but as something gentler like complete infrastructure collapse or an abrupt end to fossil fuel supplies.

In that case, even after the grocery stores are looted, you can survive without food for at least a month and maybe much longer (thank you, obesity epidemic!), but you need water within an absolute maximum of ten days or you're a goner. And in most areas, ensuring an adequate yearly supply of drinkable water is no easy feat (thank you, marmots peeing in even the clearest-looking mountain streams!). Simply, if you can't trap and treat your own water, you're toast.

One option is to use roofs. "Rainwater harvesting and catchment off roofs isn't new," says Mira Olson, civil engineer at Drexel University. The Byzantines did it residentially and the Romans did it industrially. First, tin or terra-cotta roofs are good, asphalt and shingles are bad, as is "proximity to birds," says Olson (the last due to the same reason you don't park your car beneath a roost). Also, in the first rain after a dry spell, let the first water run off the roof before connecting your system—this first flush will take with it the majority of contaminants.

But the neat part is in treatment methods. When you run out of chlorine tablets, throw in a crab shell. The shell's chitosan binds organic contaminants like bacteria, algae, and even that stray bit of marmot pee. As long as you don't eat the chunks of shell, you should be fine.

Or, "If you can filter water through a clear tube, the sunlight inactivates the bacteria for you," says Olson. Rather than killing bacteria, UV light fries bacterial DNA, making them unable to viably reproduce. You'll drink the few first bacteria, but they'll be unable to bloom in your gut. In fact, UV sterilization "pens" are available now for hiking and camping use, but forcing your harvested water to spend two to four hours percolating slowly through a clear tube in direct sunlight does the trick too.

The reward for this knowledge is the ultimate evolutionary prize: the right to repopulate the earth.

Mira Olsen works with Engineers Without Borders to design catchment and other water systems that can be used and maintained sustainably by third world populations. In its own way, third world engineering is very *Mad Max*.

BE A TRENDSETTER

Simon Levin EVOLUTIONARY BIOLOGY, PRINCETON UNIVERSITY

In 1972 Tony Alva jumped a fence to covertly skate a dry pool near California's Venice Beach neighborhood. Soon, a core group of Venice surfers-turned-skaters, including Stacy Peralta, made pool poaching a habit. When the police came, they ran. But now in the recessed pools of skate parks around the country, kids have made Alva's once innovative moves the norm. You know the story of *Dogtown and Z-Boys*. But how did Alva pull it off? How did this illegal, harebrained stunt become the social norm?

And how can you make your own harebrained ideas socially acceptable?

Simon Levin, evolutionary biologist at Princeton, explored the question from a slightly different angle: "In bird flocks and fish schools, you have a few individuals who think they know where they want to go, and the vast majority of individuals who are imitating," he says. Levin builds software models of these schools with his collaborator, Iain Couzin. Basically, he tags individuals as leaders or followers (or percentages thereof), connects them to others in the school, and then flips the switch on individual fish to see how the change propagates through the group. By tweaking the model until it acts like a natural school of fish, he discovers the mechanisms that allow change to flow through groups. It's like setting up a very detailed crowd of dominoes—when you knock one brick, how far and how fast does the ripple travel?

Or, that's what Levin used to do.

Now he applies the mathematics of fish changing directions to groups of people changing opinions.

"First, social change relies on distributed networks," says Levin. The opposite of "distributed" is a "well-mixed" network like that of a country with an authoritative central government, in which top-down control quickly suppresses novel opinions—nails that stick up are pounded down. "These systems are robust over short periods of time," says Levin. But when top-down control fails, the whole system is shot.

Now imagine Venice Beach in the 1970s. In this far-flung node of a distributed network, when Alva had the idea to skate a dry swimming pool, the sheriff wasn't able to kill it before it grew. These distributed networks, with pods of far-flung autonomy and an absence of top-down control, "have the capability for novel opinions and attitudes to spring up," says Levin.

So if you want to change cultural norms, you need to live in a place where the seed of your idea can take root without being summarily hit with Roundup by authority or the power of strong social norms. Perhaps innovating from a home base in Berkeley is easier than creating the same shift while based in Salt Lake City.

And the idea thus rooted can take over a population the same way a school of fish changes direction. "Individual fish or birds are attuned to the seven to ten fish or birds around them," says Levin, "thus the first to imitate a behavior are those most similar to the individual in which the behavior arises."

In the case of skating dry pools, these similar individuals were Alva's neighborhood friends, who coalesced into the Z-Boys, defining themselves based on this new skate culture. And just like closely following a leading fish's tight turn keeps following fish in the relatively safe center of the school, group members who quickly conformed to the new skateboard norms earned benefits. The Z-Boys had turf, they got girls, they were cool.

But in order for your innovation to spread beyond your posse, you need another important network feature: connectivity. The Z-Boys earned this connectivity at the 1975 Del Mar Nationals, where the pod of long haired, Vans wearing ne'er do wells rocked the socks off the clean-cut competition. The newly reformed *Skateboarding* magazine wrote a series of articles on Dogtown, and suddenly the Z-Boys had direct domino connection to kids across the country who wanted a piece of the action. The dominoes fell, and social norms changed course.

Levin points out the same progression of innovate-coalesce-connect in neckties, disallowing smoking in public places, tattoos, fingernail polish, gender equality, and recent rapid changes in the caste system of India. Today, you don't wear a tie because it's comfortable, but because it signals your membership in a group of professionals. What started as an affectation of Croatian mercenaries and earned fashion connectivity in Paris is now the social norm.

If you want to drive social norms, start by jumping a fence—any fence. Then push the idea on the seven to ten fish closest to you (see this book's entry with Eli Berman about creating a posse of obedient henchmen). Then connect your dominoes to the world at large.

Puzzle #14: Schooled by Fish

Connections in a school of fish are shown below. Imagine each step of communication loses half its influence, so that direct communication is 50 percent influential, friend-of-a-friend communication is 25 percent influential, and thrice-removed communication is 12.5 percent influential. Which of these fish has the most influence?

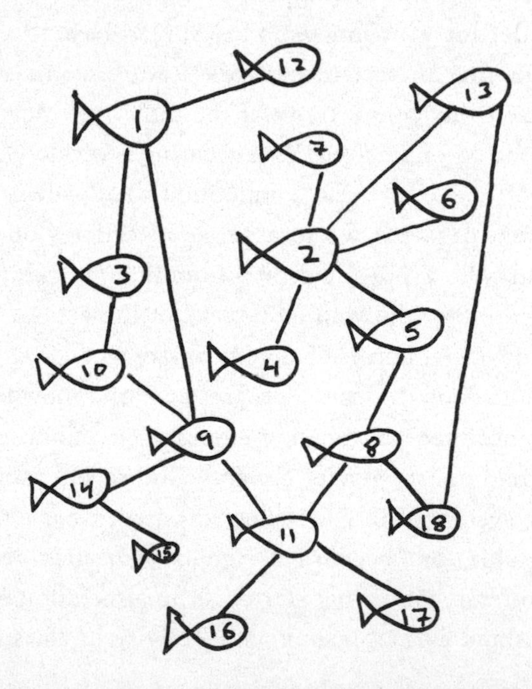

Other things that pass through networks include people through subway systems and soccer balls through World Cup teams. In 2009 Wall Street whiz kids Chris Solarz and Matt Ferresi used a cool math/computer science network analysis tool, graph theory, to discover the path of least resistance through the city's subway system, and then used their info to shave two hours off the existing record for visiting all 468 stations.

And after the 2010 World Cup, Hugo Touchette and Javier López Peña, applied mathematicians at Queen Mary, University of London, modeled teams' passing data as if a team were a network, players were nodes in the network, and the ball was the information passing through it. The resulting graphs showed team styles of play. "Mexico's passes are concentrated in the defense," says Peña, "and Spain's passes are mostly in the midfield." It also allowed them to calculate any given player's centrality—their importance to the network and thus how difficult it is for the network to adapt with the player removed. For example, in the early games of the 2010 World Cup, the Dutch player Arjen Robben had high centrality—ball movement went through him—and then in the final, he was nonexistent. Spain's aggressive marking of Arjen Robben pruned him from the system, thereby disrupting the entire flow of information through the network that was the team deemed the Clockwork Orange.

Spain was without a similar Achilles' heel: "Spain has a balanced centrality," says Touchette. In other words, it's a more flexible and thus a more robust network. If you cut off a head, the other ten heads on the pitch easily absorb the loss.

TRAIN THE BRAIN OF THE ULTIMATE INVESTOR

Antoine Bechara NEUROLOGY,
UNIVERSITY OF SOUTHERN CALIFORNIA

A quick online video search returns hugely entertaining footage of four-year-olds presented with the choice of immediately eating a marshmallow sitting on a table in front of them, or waiting for twenty minutes, at which point if their initial marshmallow remains, they earn a second marshmallow. The question, Will they wait? quickly starts to look like the question, Can they possibly physically wait? Kids writhe, kids cover their eyes, one angelic girl hollows out and eats the marshmallow center before innocently placing the gooey shell back on the table. Really, it's worth seeing.

But it's not just entertaining. The famous marshmallow test is highly predictive of success later in life. Kids who defer gratification get better SAT scores and have happier marriages.

Do you go to the dentist? Do you turn down an affair? Do you undergo surgery? Do you stay in school or reject a bribe or tie up money in investments that you could use immediately for a seven-day Caribbean cruise?

According to USC neurologist Antoine Bechara, this want/should is a teeter-totter between competing brain structures with the decision going to the weightier side (see this book's entry about oh-wow/oh-yikes shopping with Brian Knutson). "The immediate reward of a drug or a marshmallow or a bribe is processed by basic brain structures," says Bechara. The stronger the immediate reward, the more your lizard brain wants it. But then the ventral medial prefrontal cortex evaluates the consequences. "The prefrontal cortex signals that the bribe might put you in jail or the drug might take over your life," says Bechara.

That's easy: Your brain is a want/should teeter-totter.

But there are things that thumb this teeter-totter, and here's where the story gets especially interesting. For example, in 1848 the famous patient Phineas Gage blasted the "should" side of his teeter-totter clean off when the three-foot tamping rod he was using to pack blasting powder shot through his face, passed behind his left eye, and exited just above his forehead. Amazingly, not only did Gage survive, but he retained IQ and cognition. However, with the executive function portion of his brain aggressively pruned, he became impulsive to the point of dysfunction (see the tongue-in-cheek entry with Steve Schlozman on page 137 about frontal lobe degeneration and zombiism).

In addition to injury, lack of impulse control can be due to genetic abnormality. Or "traumatic early life experiences can cause dramatic rewiring of the brain in the prefrontal lobe and striatum, making a person perform much like someone with a lesion," says Bechara.

Among other shortcomings, these people are terrible investors, ruled completely by emotion without the check of logic. Bechara, along with the researchers Baba Shiv, George Loewenstein, and Hanna and Antonio Damasio, wondered how investors on the flip side of the emotion/logic teeter-totter would do—how would investors with lesions in the emotion centers of their brains perform?

The team engineered a study in which a participant is given $20.00 at the beginning of a twenty-round gambling game. In each round, the participant is given the choice to risk $1.00 on a coin flip to win $2.50. You can probably see that it's a good deal to bet every round—an expected value of $1.25 for playing versus $1.00 for declining. The result? On average, healthy subjects took home $22.80, while those with lesions to their emotion centers won $25.70.

Other researchers have shown similar is true on Wall Street. Traders who test as devoid of emotion earn more money. "Not everybody on Wall Street is a functional psychopath," says Bechara. "Instead you can learn to control your emotions. But many of the best investors do things that would be expected of functional psychopaths." So if Phineas Gage (and zombies) prioritize amygdala over frontal lobe, the brain of the ultimate investor does the opposite: pure rationality, without the influence of emotion.

And to bring this full circle, you can train this rational brain by practicing not eating the marshmallow. Delaying gratification prioritizes "should" over "want"—frontal lobe over amygdala—giving power to the rational rather than emotional areas of your brain. The more you do it, the better you'll get, not just at investing, but potentially at making decisions with the long run in mind—the delayed gratification that is so predictive of success.

But Phineas Gage's impulsivity ruined his life, and so too would living as the purely rational Spock ruin yours. In addition to training the brain of the ultimate investor, be sure you also practice leaving the functional psychopath at the office.

Among other achievements, Bechara developed the now überfamous Iowa Gambling Task, in which subjects choose a card from one of three facedown decks. In the IGT, each deck has a different payoff, and so over time, subjects learn to draw cards only from the richest deck. In fact, "learn" is a less precise word than "intuit" as it seems intuition is a quicker teacher than cognition in the IGT. More years of schooling and higher SAT scores both predict worse performance on the IGT, as these brainiacs are more likely to concoct and stick to theories of hot and cold decks, rather than listening to their hunches.

Puzzle #15: Time Discounting

Psychologists and economists know that a future reward is worth less than a significantly smaller, immediate reward. Imagine you have the choice to eat a marshmallow now or delay this gratification to earn an additional four marshmallows at some point in the future. Also imagine that the value of a marshmallow reward decays like a radioactive material, losing a quarter of its value every three minutes. At how many minutes into the future would you have earned more "value" by simply eating the one initial marshmallow immediately?

YOUR FUTURE SELF KNOWS BEST

Katherine Milkman BEHAVIORAL ECONOMICS, WHARTON SCHOOL, UNIVERSITY OF PENNSYLVANIA

It's early in the morning, everyone's asleep, and I just wandered into the kitchen to nuke a bowl of instant oatmeal. But here's the problem: Calling to me from atop the fridge are two buckets of Halloween candy. I just want the Snickers bars. Would the kids really even notice?

OK. I'm back upstairs. Those were delicious. And anyway, the microwave might've woken people up. But you know what? I'm feeling a little saccharine-saturated. My teeth are filmy and I think I hear the faint buzzing noise of excess sugar being burned in my brain like Lysol sprayed at a gas burner.

Ack! I should've had the oatmeal. What was I thinking?

The thing is, I know better. Truth be told, I did the same thing yesterday and felt the same filmy-toothed remorse. But in the face of sweet, sweet Snickers bars, something happens to me. Like Michael J. Fox in the pre–*Back to the Future* classic, I tend to wolf out a little bit.

And I'm not alone.

For example, Katherine Milkman, behavioral economist at the Wharton School, explored how people buy groceries online. Specifically, she looked at what people order when they buy for next-day delivery compared to what the same person buys when he/she orders for three days in advance. First, people spend much more when they buy for immediate consumption. And, "If you buy for rush, you buy junk," says Milkman, as shown by an increased percentage of your total haul.

Your current self buys Twinkies, while imagining what you'll need a couple days down the line puts your future self in charge and leads to the purchase of bulgur wheat and chard and other lovely things like that. (Damn, now I really want another Snickers bar.)

Milkman brought people into the lab to explore what other than time might influence splurging on junk food. After gathering folks, she explained that subjects would return tomorrow for a movie and a snack. Half the subjects were told what movie they'd be watching and half weren't. What snack did they want to accompany their movie? The uncertain half chose junk food.

Coupling these two experiments shows the power of a certain future self—it's more rational and more temperate than the self who's reading these words right now. (Admit it, you would've eaten the Snickers bars too—or maybe the Reese's cups. OK, I'm going back downstairs.)

The question is, how can you put that certain future self in charge?

First, the more certain the future is, the more power it has. So make lists, set agendas, and plan ahead to make tomorrow and the days after more definite. Second, Milkman recommends the use of a commitment device. If you want your future self to be in charge, you have to give it some leverage. For example, Milkman points to the work of Ian Ayres and Dean Karlan at Yale, who allow your future self to put out a contract on your current self. At stickK (www.stickk.com), you set a goal and bet money you'll achieve it. Then you get e-mail reminders monitoring your progress. If you fail, you lose the bet.

For you, a commitment device might be as contrived as putting your social reputation on the line (see this book's entry about behavior change with B. J. Fogg) or as simple as asking WWFSD? As you walk into the grocery store, think about your future self. Does it really want a rotisserie chicken and Ho Hos? What decisions would this future self make for you? If you can punk your psychology with this trick, great. Personally, my future self needs a little more oomph—I hereby give it the power to pilfer, burn, and then bury the ashes of all Halloween candy in the house.

Milkman also explored how people spend an unexpected $10 online grocery coupon. In classic economic theory, the mini-windfall shouldn't make a difference in your choices—you still need what you need and should spend what you spend—but as Milkman points out, "Psychologists think this should make you feel rich." And sure enough, people tend to spend this coupon on nontypical items like fresh seafood and fresh fruit. These windfall buys aren't necessarily unhealthy, but they are luxury. They're what you'd buy if you were rich.

BIGGER, STRONGER, FASTER (WITHOUT EXERCISING)

Ronald Evans MOLECULAR BIOLOGY, SALK INSTITUTE

"The longstanding field of muscle physiology says that better performance is achieved only through training," says Ronald Evans, molecular biologist at the Salk Institute and Howard Hughes Medical Institute. In other words, "you may have the innate ability to be the fastest swimmer," says Evans, "but if you don't work hard, you'll be overtaken by the second-fastest swimmer."

Bummer. Down that line of reasoning lies long hours in the gym and self-denial in the face of Cherry Garcia.

But between exercise and muscle development is an important step. "The cell nucleus is the control system," says Evans. "Done right, you can make the nucleus undergo the changes it would experience during exercise, without exercise."

Booyah!

Unfortunately this cellular sleight of hand isn't as simple as visualizing running or watching *Sweating to the Oldies* while sucking an energy drink. Instead, the story starts with the body's chemical form of energy: ATP. When you exercise, your cells' mitochondria convert fat, carbs, or really whatever else is floating around your midsection into ATP, which you then break down to create energy and a by-product called AMP. More exercise equals more ATP use and thus more AMP by-product. So when the body detects AMP, it assumes it's exercising and burns more fat, carbs, and midsection to keep pace with its expected needs. Upon detecting AMP, your body also increases the rate of muscle building, which repairs the natural damage of exercise and beefs up muscle reserves in preparation for what it sees as likely future demands.

The drug AICAR mimics AMP.

When you inject it, your body thinks you've exercised. You burn more sugars and build more muscle, but, "Really only the signal of exercise has been given," says Evans. In the lab, mice on AICAR lost weight and increased endurance even when given a high-fat diet.

So simply get a prescription for AICAR and you'll qualify for the Boston Marathon while consuming all the Cherry Garcia and Krispy Kreme donuts your trans-fat-choked heart desires.

Only, there's a catch.

"There are two problems with this drug: It's [only] injectable, and it's old," says Evans. Simply, drugs aren't created to cure disease or increase health. They're created to make money. And the market doesn't want to inject. Also, with AICAR being old and off-patent, any drug company in the world can make it, and so any company that put $100 million into the R&D needed to push a human-ready drug through the FDA would face immediate market competition from generics.

So don't look for AICAR anytime soon.

But there's another pathway you can punk.

PPR-delta is a nuclear receptor—it hangs out on a nucleus's wall, waving like a sea anemone until it sees the molecule it wants, at which point it grabs it and relays the information of the catch inside the nucleus. What PPR-delta grabs is fat, and when it gets it, cells know that instead of conserving scarce resources, a glut is floating around your bloodstream and they can burn fat quickly. Evans and others have engineered synthetic molecules to mimic this effect—keep your eyes peeled for drug release in the next few years.

Until then, ditch saturated fats.

PPR-delta doesn't bind saturated fat, which goes straight into your body's storeroom without signaling your body to increase its burn rate. But the PPR-delta anemones love mono- and polyunsaturated fats—they grab them from your bloodstream and tell your body to get cranking. Foods high in omega-3s (fish) or resveratrol (red wine!) present PPR-delta only the fats it can grab and that thus fuel your body's fire, and not the saturated fat that quickly makes one unable to see one's toes. Dairy products consistently have the highest saturated fat percentage, and walnuts have one of the lowest. In oils, stay away from coconut and palm, and instead go for corn or flaxseed.

Evans's work shows that stem cells continually spit out new neurons in two areas of the brain: the olfactory bulb and the hippocampus. Once you're an adult, many of these new neurons are born and then immediately die, but some are woven into the architecture of the brain. New neurons in the olfactory bulb may allow you to smell better in later life (as it were), while tests with mice show that new neurons in the hippocampus may allow you continue coding new memories and learning new things. Evans found that both physical and mental exercise boost the rate at which neural stem cells spit out new neurons.

Researchers at McMaster University showed that lifting light weights to exhaustion builds as much muscle as lifting heavy weights. The key, they found, is muscle fatigue—and while lifting heavy weights might be a shortcut to this fatigue, the same addition of muscle was created by lifting lighter weights at higher reps.

SEXY OF VOICE, SEXY OF BODY

Gordon Gallup EVOLUTIONARY PSYCHOLOGY, UNIVERSITY OF ALBANY

Changing your body shape is time-consuming and effortful, requiring things like exercising and eating less (unless you read this book carefully). But adopting a sexy voice? With the help of University of Albany evolutionary psychologist Gordon Gallup, you can do it today.

Gallup had undergrads count to ten in a tape recorder and then played back these recordings to their peers. Even without flirtatious or smoldering content, there was strong agreement on which voices were sexy and which were not. And Gallup showed that these sexy voices were strong predictors of sexy bodies—sexy-voiced men had higher shoulder-to-hip ratios, and sexy-voiced women had lower waist-to-hip ratios. These sexy voices also predicted an earlier age of first sexual experience and higher total number of sex partners. In short, a sexy voice actually is a good predictor of sexiness.

So what were the characteristics of these sexy voices?

If you've seen any of the *Toy Story* movies, you know what makes a sexy male voice—Tim Allen as Buzz Lightyear is sexier than Tom Hanks as Woody. There's very clear and definite evidence that a low male voice is sexier, and Gallup points out that this low voice may be the product of the same hit of testosterone during puberty that creates desirable shoulder-to-hip ratios.

But the female sexy voice is trickier and independent of high or low pitch. Instead, the strongest factor in the sexy female voice is breathiness. We have two vocal cords, with a slight gap between them—women tend to have a bigger gap than men, and this is what creates breathiness. The bigger the gap, the more breathiness, and perhaps the more estrogen during puberty.

But here's the important part: Vocal attractiveness creates the perception of physical attractiveness. If a date hears your sexy voice, he or she expects a sexy person, and these expectations mean that when you meet, your date will, in fact, rate your physical attractiveness higher than if you'd had a mediocre voice. Why bother with a month's crash diet and agro iron-pumping when you can get a bump in beauty simply by talking sexy?

"During a kiss there's a rich, complicated exchange of information, that we think may activate hardwired systems to assess health, vitality, and thus genetic fitness of potential mates," says Gordon Gallup.

But if you're measuring success by number of progeny, men and women have very different goals—a man does best when he eats shoots and leaves (as it were), "whereas for women, having sex is just the start," says Gallup, "after which is weeks, months, and years of pregnancy, breastfeeding, and child care."

Gallup found that these different evolutionary goals lead to gender-specific uses of kissing. "Males are much more likely to attempt to initiate with an open mouth and much more likely to kiss with the tongue," says Gallup. This is sexual kissing and men use it as a tick on the preflight checklist. Whereas, "Females kiss not only during courtship and mate assessment, but to monitor the status of a committed relationship," says Gallup. For women, kissing is a way to get information that's otherwise hard to get.

SPOTTING SINCERITY—A SLOW "YES" MEANS "NO"

Colin Camerer NEUROECONOMICS,
CALIFORNIA INSTITUTE OF TECHNOLOGY

It's the end of what seemed like a good first date. You ask if he'll call and he says ". . . Yes!" But will he really?

"Slow means 'no,'" says Colin Camerer, economist and neuroscientist at Caltech. He explains that in consumer surveys, political polling, and many other situations in which the person questioned knows what the questioner wants to hear, people are likely to please during the conversation but fail to follow through. Would you buy this awesome product the nice person on the phone just spent two minutes explaining? [Pause] Yes. Would you vote for the political candidate the caller's stumping for? [Pause] Yes. Should you expect to hear from your date again soon? [Pause] Yes, of course!

This is known as the yes bias, and it's vexed pollsters from time immemorial.

But imagine we weren't dependent on the notoriously inaccurate words that come from people's mouths. Suppose, instead, we could look in consumers' or voters' or daters' brains for their opinions.

Camerer did just that. "What we found," he says, "is that hypothetical choices are a fifth of a second faster than real choices." People decide if they would (hypothetically) vote or buy or call very quickly. And so to a hypothetical question, a quick response is a true response. If there's a fifth of a second lag, it's likely due to the time it takes politeness the overrule the honest impulse—spackling the veneer that will please the questioner over the true answer that wouldn't. Lying takes longer.

But when making real decisions, an extra area of the brain is activated—the cingulate cortex. "It's like a second level of checking," says Camerer. For example, when you ask the very real question (with real consequences) of whether your date would like to kiss, it takes a fifth of a second to double-check the impulse. In real choices there should be a short delay, and you should trust the answer.

So spotting sincerity first requires recognizing the type of question you're asking—if it's a real question, you should expect a slight delay, followed by the true answer; but when you ask a yes/no question about any hypothetical future action—will he call?—the answer should be fast. Watch for a delay. If "yes" spits slowly, it may be politeness and the desire to please overriding the real answer: no.

In that fifth of a second, you can see the brain's true intent.

YOU SUCK, SO I ROCK

David Dunning PSYCHOLOGY, CORNELL UNIVERSITY

Cornell psychologist David Dunning asked how many students would buy daffodils in an upcoming fund-raiser for the American Cancer Society. A full 80 percent of these saintly students said they would certainly purchase a flower, though they were less rosy in their predictions of peers' willingness to buy, opining that only 50 percent overall would pony up for the cause. You might have guessed the punch line: After the fund-raiser, only 43 percent of students actually bought flowers.

Similarly, he asked how many students would vote in the then upcoming November elections. Eighty-four percent said they'd vote, and they expected 67 percent of their peers to vote. The tale of the tape was 68 percent turnout.

"People are pretty accurate in their judgments of others," says Dunning. "But terrible in their judgments of themselves." This is why the vast majority of drivers and 94 percent of the college professors Dunning surveyed consider themselves "above average." It doesn't take a Fields Medal to see that's mathematically impossible.

And so across the board we overestimate our goodness while pretty much nailing predictions of others' actions.

But something cool happens when you go from concrete predictions of yes/no type behaviors to evaluations of others in which there's wiggle room. How intelligent or how good of a leader is someone? These evaluations are much more subjective than asking how many peers will buy a daffodil. To see if we're as accurate with subjective evaluations, Dunning brought college sophomores ("my species," he says) into the lab.

What he found is that we have very specific templates that we use to measure others. Simply, the template is the person doing the measuring. Is someone intelligent? Is someone a good leader? Well, if they're like us, then yes in both cases. And, "If you put someone's self-esteem under pressure by making them fail a task or something similar, then people even more strongly positively judge others who are like them," says Dunning. When you're down, you boost similar others as a way to get back your own lost sense of self. (Is this why blue-collar America cited the "just like me" quality when voting for Bush II?)

"If you step outside the lab, people show the same behaviors," says Dunning. For example, he asked nontenured professors how many published papers should be expected in order to gain tenure. It was a relatively low number compared to the number of papers that tenured professors thought should be required. Similarly, he asked college sophomores if others with certain math SAT scores were "mathematically gifted." Generally, students saw anyone who scored above their own SAT result as gifted.

We are the bar we set for others.

What's also cool is that the strength of this effect depends on how much we care about the topic. In the context of a test that's supposedly a gateway into a certain career, students who were premed, prelaw, or prebusiness set much more self-centered targets for others if the test was relevant to their specific career choice.

Reverse engineering this allows you to test how strongly a person feels about any topic. Are your friends quick to judge and likely to set the mark very close to their own behaviors when evaluating others' parenting? Or coolness? Or fashion sense? Or attention to detail? Or musical taste? Or . . . anything, really? By noticing these self-centered judgments, you can discover how strongly people care.

The Dunning-Kruger effect describes people who are blind to their own stupidity. Classically, people who scored in the lowest 12 percent in Dunning's tests of humor, logic, and grammar estimated they had scored in the top 62 percent. People who scored higher were much more accurate in their estimates.

Other researchers at Cornell had students come up with movie ideas and then pitch them to other students. In written form, narcissists' pitches were no more convincing than those of their peers. But when narcissists pitched their movie ideas in person, they were a full 50 percent more well received than their peers'. The conclusion is this: The narcissist in your group shouldn't be allowed to sculpt the product, but should be encouraged to present it.

PROOF YOURSELF AGAINST SENSATIONALIZED STATS

Keith Devlin MATHEMATICS, STANFORD UNIVERSITY

WARNING: a long and somewhat involved path of (very cool) statistics lies ahead.

Keith Devlin is NPR's "Math Guy," a World Economic Forum fellow, and math professor at Stanford. And so he thinks about things differently than the world at large. For example, in his monthly column "Devlin's Angle," he quotes the following problem, originally designed by puzzle master Gary Foshee: "I tell you that I have two children, and that (at least) one of them is a boy born on Tuesday. What probability should you assign to the event that I have two boys?"

Does this sound like a bunch of confounding mumbo jumbo meant to obscure the obvious fact that the other kid has exactly 50/50 chance of being a boy and so if one kid's definitely a boy, the probability of them both being boys is one in two? Yes, yes it does.

But that's not the case.

Without the "Tuesday" part, this is a famous problem first published in *Scientific American* by the venerable mathematician and puzzler Martin Gardner. Imagine the possible genders and birth orders of two kids: B-B, B-G, G-B, G-G. Now, in Gardner's problem you know that at least one child is a boy, so you can nix only G-G as a possibility, leaving B-B, B-G, and G-B. In only one of these remaining three possibilities are both children boys, so instead of the knee-jerk one in two probability any sane person would expect, mathematicians like Devlin give only a one in three probability that, given one child is a boy, both kids are boys.

Yikes.

But the Tuesday bit can't possibly matter, can it?

"It depends if you ask a mathematician or a statistician," says

Devlin. The mathematician would simply extend the possibilities that were available in the original puzzle and then nix the possibilities that could be nixed. If we didn't know that one of the kids was born on a Tuesday, our possibilities would be all the possible crosses of: B-Mo, B-Tu, B-We, B-Th, B-Fr, B-Sa, B-Su, with G-Mo, G-Tu, G-We, G-Th, G-Fr, G-Sa, G-Su.

Cool so far?

Now, you know that either the first or the second child is a boy born on Tuesday, and here's how Devlin lays out the revised possibilities:

- First child B-Tu, second child: B-Mo, B-Tu, B-We, B-Th, B-Fr, B-Sa, B-Su, G-Mo, G-Tu, G-We, G-Th, G-Fr, G-Sa, G-Su.
- Second child B-Tu, first child: B-Mo, B-We, B-Th, B-Fr, B-Sa, B-Su, G-Mo, G-Tu, G-We, G-Th, G-Fr, G-Sa, G-Su.

Since "both boys born on Tuesday" is already listed in the first set, we don't need to list it again in the second, making 27 (instead of 28) possible combinations of gender and day of the week for two kids, if at least one is a boy born on Tuesday. And of these 27 possibilities, 13 of them include a second boy. So the answer is (instead of a one in two or one in three chance) a 13/27 chance that both will be boys.

D'you hear that crackling sound? That's the sound of your neurons trying to deal with the previous five hundred words. Don't say you weren't warned. But stick with it. It's worth it. You can do it.

Now, on to statisticians, who take another view entirely. To them it matters what else could have been said and the interpretations that can pop up when math is released into the real world. "For example," says Devlin, "we're taught that multiplication is commutative, that 3×4 is the same as 4×3; but in the real world three bags of four apples isn't the same as four bags of three apples." Similarly, he points out in his blog that if you're told that a quarter pound of ham costs $2 and then asked what three pounds will cost, a mathematician would tell you $24, but a statistician who's been to a supermarket knows there's not enough information to answer the question—of course, every supermarket discounts for bulk.

In the case of the Tuesday boy problem, imagine you're from a culture that requires you to speak about an elder child first, before mentioning the younger. That means it's the eldest child who's the boy, and you rule out both G-G (as before) but also G-B, leaving the possibilities BB and BG, and a one in two probability of both being boys.

So there are two broad interpretations of almost all real-world numbers problems—the stripped-down, mathematicians' approach and the interpretive statisticians' approach. And it's in this wiggle room of interpretation where pure math hits the real world that misleading statistics are born. For example, in 1993 the columnist George Will was mathematically correct when he wrote in the *Washington Post* that "the ten states with the lowest per-pupil spending included four—North Dakota, South Dakota, Tennessee, Utah—among the ten states with the top SAT scores. Only one of the ten states with the highest per-pupil expenditures—Wisconsin—was among the ten states with the highest SAT scores. New Jersey has the highest per-pupil expenditures, an astonishing $10,561 . . . New Jersey's rank regarding SAT scores? Thirty-ninth."

Take a minute and see if you can spot the moment at which pure math became a misleading statistic.

I found this quote in a 1999 article in the *Journal of Statistics Education* that points out one important fact: In New Jersey all college-bound students take the SAT, whereas in North Dakota, South Dakota, Tennessee, and Utah, only the kids applying to out-of-state schools take the SAT. And you can bet these students applying out of state are the cream of the crop. This is selection bias, and it pops up everywhere. Yes, it seems odd that nine out of ten dentists recommend Crass toothpaste, and nine out of ten also recommend Goldgate, but it's as easy as finding the right ten dentists to ask.

Or take the following headline (from WorldHealth.net), which demonstrates a trick central to a pop science writer's existence: SINCERE SMILING PROMOTES LONGEVITY. Sure enough, the data in the original study show that people who flash sincere smiles in photographs live longer—the original study title is SMILE INTENSITY IN PHOTOGRAPHS PREDICTS LONGEVITY.

Again, take a minute and see if you can spot the difference.

The trick is that the study demonstrates correlation, while the article implies causation. Does a Duchenne smile "predict" longevity? Yes. Does it "promote" longevity? Not necessarily. Mightn't it be more likely that these smilers are happy and that something in happiness and not the smile itself actually promotes longevity? Similarly, it's mathematically correct that gun owners have 2.7 times the chance of being murdered compared to non-gun owners. Does owning a gun cause the owner to be murdered, or might it be something in the character of people likely to own guns?

For another, take the 2010 claim by health reform director Nancy-Ann DeParle that due to the then recently passed health care bill, the average annual cost of insurance coverage would drop by one thousand dollars by 2019. Taken at face value, it's true. But the reason it's true is that nearly free health care would be extended to 32 million Americans who were currently without care, meaning that the cost to people who were already insured in 2010 would actually go up to cover the newly added.

This is an apples-to-oranges comparison, like decrying the increase in the average cost of a gallon of gas from $0.99/gal in February 1992 to $3.38/gal in February 2011 without adjusting for inflation. You can't compare the two, because the rules of comparison have changed. On the flip side of the political spectrum, conservative UK politician Chris Grayling cited a 35 percent increase in "violent" crime starting in 2002 as evidence of failed liberal law enforcement policies. But 2002 was the year civilians and not police were given the right to designate a crime "violent," and many chose to see violence where the police might not have. The "35 percent increase" was the difference between apples and oranges.

Finally, take data showing that the TSA misses 5 percent of people hired to test air security by trying to smuggle dangerous contraband. Yikes! One in twenty people sitting around you on the plane is packing a shoe bomb!

What's the error?

It's in sampling. Though some days it feels this way, not everyone is out to get you. In fact, imagine that even one of the two million passengers who try to fly over the United States every day is a deadly terrorist, and imagine the TSA misses 5 percent of them. This means that one in 40 million people flying is a deadly terrorist. Even on a Boeing 767 with a 300-person seating capacity, you'd have to fly more than 130,000 times to sit on a plane with a terrorist. (OK, that's misleading too: Statisticians would point out that a 1 in 130,000 chance means you could be on a plane with a terrorist at any point, it's just not ever very likely.) Compare that to a 1 in 100 lifetime chance of dying in a car crash. Actually, please do, because that's a mathematically correct, misleading statistic too—what if you don't drive, or drive cautiously, or are already over age twenty-five?

So the moral of this long and somewhat convoluted tale is that first there's math, then there's stats, and finally there are headlines. And like a game of telephone, it's easy to lose meaning along the way due to things like selection bias, correlation/causation, apples/oranges, and population error.

Mark Twain said there are lies, damned lies, and statistics.

Illuminating this, renowned business professor Aaron Levenstein said that statistics are like bikinis—what they reveal is suggestive but what they conceal is vital. But not for you. You now know how to reveal what is vital.

Puzzle #16: October Boy

If I tell you that I have two children, both born in October, and at least one a boy born on a day whose date contains at least one "1," then what is the probability that both my children are boys?

AVOID THE CARPLIKE STARE OF CHOICE PARALYSIS

Jonah Berger DECISION SCIENCE, WHARTON SCHOOL, UNIVERSITY OF PENNSYLVANIA

Next to the box of Cheerios on the grocery store's thirty-yard-long cereal shelf sits a box of store-brand Rolled O's. And there you stand, staring carplike at the two boxes, transfixed, slack-jawed—but tormented inside! You expected the choice to be easy and now for some reason it's . . . not. You've been mesmerized by choice paralysis and you aren't going anywhere soon.

Last night you did the same thing online with flight options. Last month you spent a combined twelve hours agonizing over what shade of white to paint your kitchen.

"Generally, important decisions take longer," says Jonah Berger of the Wharton School. Good, great, we expect them to, and so we're neither surprised nor frustrated when deciding between colleges or job offers or real estate options is a slow and difficult process.

But Berger found that something interesting happens when a trivial decision turns out to be difficult. "By the fact that it takes longer, we infer that it's important," says Berger, "and because it now seems important, we automatically give the decision more time."

Remember Niro Sivanathan's consumption quicksand, in which people in debt feel bad about themselves and so consume esteem goods on credit, putting them further in debt and thus making them feel even worse about themselves and more likely to consume esteem goods on credit? Well, this is a similar feedback loop: Once you've spent time on a trivial decision, you give it the veneer of an important decision, and you're trapped. The longer it takes, the longer it's going to take, and the more likely you are to find yourself drooling while staring cross-eyed at boxes of cereal.

Maybe you should read the nutrition panel one more time in hopes it will make the difference? Maybe you should ask other customers? Should you call your spouse?

Berger says the key in breaking choice paralysis is to stop it before it starts—or barring that, stop it in its infant stages before your mind becomes figgy pudding. If you can predict an upcoming decision of little consequence that—despite its unimportance—can provide closely matched and vexing options, set a time limit. In twenty minutes you will click BUY on the best airplane ticket you've found thus far. Or at the end of five minutes, you'll grab whatever Creative Commons image seems best to head your blog post. Or in thirty seconds, you'll be out of the cereal aisle.

Or imagine the initial surprise of a trivial/difficult decision that goes something like, Huh, I wonder if toothbrush bristles in square or circular designs remove the most plaque? Recognize trivial/difficult and counteract it quickly by setting a time limit. Act now, before it's too late.

"Double Rainbow," the "Charlie Bit My Finger!" kid, the surprised kitty, the Evian roller babies, the "Paparazzi" talent show kid, the "BP Spills Coffee" video, the "Bimbo Waka Waka" dancing baby—these are videos that "went viral" as the kids say these days, becoming massive cultural phenomena on the scale of the Declaration of Independence, the Constitution, and "Where's the beef?"

Jonah Berger knows how you can go viral too.

He explored the *New York Times* archives for factors that make articles highly shared. "Generally, we want to put people in good moods," says Berger, and so we share surprising and/or humorous positive content (that revelation may be neither surprising nor humorous). But Berger also found that certain negative emotions are highly shared, including vids and articles that create anxiety, anger, or outrage. It's arousal that predicts content sharing—both on the happy/surprised/humorous side and on the angry/outraged/incensed side. Simply, go big or doom your content to one-and-done. Or as *The Economist* described his finding, "It's better to be reviled than ignored."

THE POWER OF A CONNECTED MINORITY

Michael Kearns COMPUTER SCIENCE,
UNIVERSITY OF PENNSYLVANIA

Generally, there are two ways to study networks. One is by creating mathematical models—like Simon Levin at Princeton, who we met in the entry about trendsetting and fish schools—and then poking and prodding these models in various ways. The other is to study existing networks, which allows you to see how behaviors or information flow in the real world (see, for instance, the book *Connected*, which details the ways behaviors like smoking and obesity flow through a social network in a

Massachusetts town). The first allows you to adjust the network design to see how tweaks affect its function. The second allows you to see real effects in real people.

But what if you could do both, at the same time?

Michael Kearns found a way to have his cake and eat it too. "About six years ago I started running these behavioral lab experiments in which I bring moderately large groups of people into the lab, impose various network structures, give them a game to play for real money, and study how they do," says Kearns, CS and information science guru at the University of Pennsylvania and the Wharton School. Thus he could design and tweak the network, while also seeing how real people act within it.

For example, in one of his games, subjects tried to coordinate colors. Kearns gathered thirty-six undergrads and stuck them in a room so that they could only see certain of their neighbors, then he started a one-minute timer. Everyone in the room could display red or blue, and if at any time in that one minute everyone coordinated on either color, the whole room got paid. If not, no payday for the undergrads. After the minute, Kearns switched the network structure, and they played again.

So there was high incentive for agreement. "We designed this just after the 2008 democratic primaries," says Kearns, in which you might remember Democrats had a high incentive for agreement—the sooner Dems could coordinate on Clinton or Obama, the sooner they could start hacking at the throats of Republicans instead of at one another. This proved challenging because, for one reason, while unanimity was good for all, people within the network tended to feel strongly that either Clinton or Obama was more good.

Similarly, Kearns threw into the mix of his lab games unequal payoffs—for some people, coordinating on red paid $1.50 while agreeing on blue paid only $0.50. For others, the reverse was true. So you'd really rather agree on your high-paying color, but barring that, the other's better than nothing. Did these networks still get paid, or did they devolve into infighting and general uncoordinated badness in which everyone suffered?

It depended on the network.

For example, in one experiment Kearns gave thirty players a blue preference and only six players an equal and opposite red preference. But he stuck the shorthanded red players in special spots in the network, with the largest number of neighbors. "We ran twenty-seven experiments like this," says Kearns, "and in twenty-four of these, the network was able to reach an agreement." Can you guess which color they agreed on? In every case, it was the preference of the highly connected minority—little, social red carried the day. "The minority opinion will dominate the outcome if the minority is sufficiently well connected," says Kearns. This might remind you of the effect of special-interest lobbyists.

You also might remember the earlier Simon Levin story, in which he showed mathematically that the behavior of a small, committed minority needed connectivity to flow through a population and change social norms. Well, you can see the mathematical model in human action in Kearns's lab.

But one interesting finding is that even within these scripted networks in which Kearns says he "tries to shoehorn human subjects into settings in which they perform like ants," personality continues to influence outcomes. One aspect of personality that's especially clear in coordination games is stubbornness—are you willing to switch your color in the face of a developing majority that disagrees with you? But the effect of stubbornness isn't necessarily all bad, as you might expect. Sure, if a network includes too much stubbornness, players end up entrenched in their little, opposing fiefdoms. But its opposite is equally detrimental—if everyone's too willing to flip-flop, the network does just that, oscillating wildly between colors without ever coming to full consensus on either.

This is like the group of indecisive friends trying to pick a restaurant. Maybe we should eat Thai! Sure. Or what about Mexican? Um, OK. Or Chinese? Sounds good. And you end up getting all muddled in overagreement. At some point the network needs some stubbornness.

In another game, Kearns gave humans a game that's classically hard for computers. In the map-coloring puzzle, you have four colors and must shade the countries on a map so that no two neighboring countries are the same color. If tiny Switzerland goes orange, it affects the color of China, and the rippling of this change quickly requires massive computational chutzpah.

But humans role-playing countries color themselves rather quickly. "One lesson I've learned that transcends all types of experiments," says Kearns, "is that I'm surprised how good people are at this stuff." He points to this as hope for more and more ambitious crowdsourcing.

Still, there are things that computers do better than humans, and things that one brain does better than many. "If a problem can be broken into a gazillion pieces, you can crowdsource," says Kearns. But if the pieces themselves require coordination, a problem may still best be solved by good old-fashioned expertise. I apologize in advance for the following sports simile (and not even a sport I play), but it's like golf: Sure you could crowdsource a hole, with hundreds of people teeing off and then playing only the best ball. But wouldn't this problem be more efficiently solved by pre-2009 Tiger Woods?

Imagine your problem. Any problem.

Is it "chunkable," like needing thirty recipes for lightning-fast dinners or the best Monty Python quotes or suggestions from your geeked-out friends for scientists to interview for a book you're writing? If so, you might throw it out to FB or Twitter or whatever social networking site seems most applicable (be sure to provide incentive, likely framing it as entertainment or offering some sort of credit to the solvers). If the problem requires backstory and foresight, consider looking up a leading expert or making yourself into one. Or is it simply a question of firepower? Likely, there's software and/or a bigger, badder box to help with that.

And then join Kearns in hoping that someday soon there will be a middle path that uses all three (see following coolness).

"I have a research fantasy that we're far from but that I like to think about sometimes," says Kearns. Today there exist "compilers" that take a computational problem and recruit components from a network of computers to solve it. This allows you to design a problem without worrying about memory management, or CPUs, or virtual versus physical memory, or any of the other computational limits of your solving system (within reason). "I like to imagine a crowdsourcing compiler," says Kearns. This compiler would break down a problem into its components and then recruit the optimal tool for solving each. Maybe one chunk requires expertise—the compiler would scroll through the Proceedings of the National Academy of Sciences publications until finding, recruiting, and motivating the top expert. One chunk could simply be computed, and the compiler would pull together the resources for it. And another component might best be crowdsourced, and the compiler would put out feelers into the human online world, creating an incentive like a game or a salary that gets a human network to solve the needed piece.

"We're moving into a new era," say Kearns, "in which human computing interfaces with computer computing." This isn't the old sci-fi scenario of übertech dominating humans, nor is it today's model of humans using tech as tool, but a completely new scenario in which humans and the machines we've created collaborate to solve problems in ways neither could possibly do on their own.

Puzzle #17: Map Problem

Use only four colors to shade the following map so that no touching states share the same color.

CREATE A KICK-ASS TRIBE, ANY TRIBE

David Logan ORGANIZATIONAL BEHAVIOR, UNIVERSITY OF SOUTHERN CALIFORNIA

If you've ever watched *Survivor*, you know that not all tribes are created equal. Some are rancorous and repressive, me-centered and backstabbing, while others are cooperative and inclusive, honest, and even idealistic. David Logan, expert in organizational communication at USC's Marshall School of Business, knows how to make your tribe the latter.

As you might imagine, Logan's studied these tribes mostly in the context of businesses, which he divides into five tribal stages.

The first he defines with the phrase "life sucks." "It's not that people in these organizations don't have individual core values but that the organizational culture says you have to undermine these values to survive," he says. You may be forced to cheat to get ahead in the company or encouraged to lie to customers. Thus the battle between core and company values and the overall sucking of life.

In the next tribal level, it's not that life sucks as a whole, only that each individual thinks "my life sucks." "Employees say 'I made suggestions but nobody listened,' or otherwise deflect accountability," says Logan.

Stage three includes 48 percent of the organizations Logan's documented in his eight-and-ongoing years of study. This stage is defined by the idea that "I'm great and you're not," he says. People might have positive individual relationships with many others in the tribe, but there's little coming together. You might solicit other group members to gain agreement for your ideas, but it creates little pods of stage two around the core group.

Leveraging the spirit born of shared values, 22 percent of tribes are able to make the leap from "I'm great" to "We're great." This is stage four—"the first stage at which the group becomes aware of its tribalness," says Logan. You can tell you're there when a two-person conversation that's interrupted absorbs and integrates the interrupter—if you're all truly in the same tribe, there's every reason to be inclusive and none to be exclusive.

So that's it—the four stages of tribal development. You can read more about it in Logan's book *Tribal Leadership* (with John King and Halee Fischer-Wright).

Only, that's not it. There's a fifth stage, "and these groups create amazing things," says Logan, "like reconciliation in South Africa or Apple famously asking the question, How can I create a computer so simple that even my mom could use it?" The theme of a stage-five tribe is "life is great," but the problem is that stage-five tribes can be idealistic to the point of being dreamy and not tied to the market, "like an Internet start-up that says 'We don't need cash, we've got clicks!' " says Logan. In his view, it's ideal to stay at stage four, while infrequently dipping into stage five to ask, How do we make history? or How do we shake up the industry? "Stage five is pure leadership," says Logan, pointing out that stage four is a nice mix of leadership and management, while stage three is pure management drowning out leadership, and below that not even management functions.

So that's great: five stages of tribal development. But more important than defining these stages is the ability to move up the food chain. How can you design a business with stage four in mind?

If you're starting from scratch, rather than hiring people at the start-up level who have the longest resumes, "first, find your own values," says Logan. "Then find people who share these values." Build around a value statement like Zappo's "We believe in doing more with less."

Once you grow past a small pod of naturally like-minded collaborators, "create initiatives that express these core values," says Logan. In addition to giving new employees a dinner-party answer to the question, What does your company do?, give them an answer to the question, What does your company believe in? Values give employees something to coalesce around, and this coming together creates a strong tribe.

"If you look at the early Jedi, they became inept and powerless by denying the Dark Side," says Logan, now speaking my language. "But at the end of *Return of the Jedi*, what you see is that Luke didn't defeat evil, but integrated it. As Luke rebuilds the Jedi, will they still be monklike and celibate? No, they'll balance the Light and Dark Sides."

To Logan, the same balance is true of good leaders. "My theory is that leaders have a larger dark side than most of us," he says. "They can tap into its power, but are always at risk of being destroyed by it." Jimmy Carter is a wonderful person, but was a terrible president, "partly because he never tapped into his dark side," says Logan. In fact, it's unclear that Carter even had one.

There's a huge body of research on individual intelligence, especially how to measure it, what predicts it, and how to train it. But researchers at Carnegie Mellon just recently provided the first direct evidence for a fixed collective intelligence in groups. Interestingly, factors you might assume made smart groups—including group cohesion, motivation, and satisfaction—had no effect. But there were three things that across many studies created smarter groups: (1) social sensitivity; (2) little variance in members' number of speaking turns—the conversation wasn't dominated by one voice; and (3) the proportion of members who were female—though this was due in part to social sensitivity.

GOVERNMENT, GOD, OR SELF: WHERE DO YOU GET CONTROL?

Aaron Kay SOCIAL PSYCHOLOGY, DUKE UNIVERSITY

I like to believe both that the early bird catches the worm, and that he who mischief hatcheth, mischief catcheth. The root of this desire is surely the fact that I get up early and that for at least the last handful of years I've kept my mischief hatching to a minimum—and I like to think that my saintly actions will lead to reward. I also like to believe that if I drive well I will avoid accidents, that if I read to my kids and install the right preschool math applications on my smartphone they will go to Yale, and that if I eat well and exercise I can avoid unhealthy things like dying.

Duke social psychologist Aaron Kay points out that I'm not alone. "In the Western world, people like to believe in a high degree of personal control," says Kay, "that whatever happens, good or bad, is controlled by your actions." But sometimes it's a difficult belief to maintain sometimes slackers win the lottery while saints are hit by falling pianos. "When we're reminded of randomness, it creates anxiety," says Kay, "and when we feel anxious we want to believe that even if we don't have control, something does."

By reminding people of this randomness in lab settings, he's shown that people with diminished personal control are more likely to turn to authoritarian gods or governments. If I wake up early and there are simply no worms, I want to believe that there's a reason for that lack of worms. God or the government must be to blame—certainly someone must be driving this funhouse ride, right?

Imagine a personal, internal teeter-totter that needs to stay level in order to make everything copacetic with the world (the angle of tilt is your level of anxiety). On one side is control, made up of personal control, governmental control, and religious control. And on the other side are the events of the world—sometimes a relatively orderly baseline and sometimes a wild jumble of chance.

Now imagine removing some weight from personal control. To keep your metaphysical teeter-totter in balance you need increased government or religious control (or both).

Now imagine plucking a weight from governmental control. Kay showed that in the period of governmental uncertainty before a major election, belief in God goes up (reduced governmental control balanced by increased religious control). Similarly, it seems in the United States as if high religious control is associated with the desire for low governmental control. And, "In countries with little personal or governmental control, you may find more belief channeled into the supernatural option," says Kay.

However, just as the teeter-totter tipping away from control creates anxiety that people heal by increasing government, religious, or personal control, when the teeter-totter tips toward too much control, people feel oppressed and try to get out from under its thumb. This is an authoritarian government's revolutionary proletariat or a controlling parent's teenage daughter.

So the key, as implied by the now overused simile of a teeter-totter, is that of balance. I'm sure you can imagine how to get rid of control in excess of what you need. But if you're feeling like Earth is tumbling toward the Sun, it can be trickier to take the control you want. Certainly, you can join a controlling church or political party (or even adopt a personal belief in an all-powerful god), but so too can you grab the bull by the horns and increase your personal control of life. Make the present more definite with a daily schedule, making sure to include time that you spend according to your own choosing (see this book's entry with Sheena Iyengar). And make the future definite with lists, agendas, and long-term life plans.

By taking control of the world around you, you can decrease the anxiety born of a topsy-turvy world.

Aaron Kay and collaborators had Canadian women read paragraphs about emigration, half of which implied that leaving the country would get easier in the next five years, and half of which implied it would get harder. Then they all read the same paragraph about gender inequality in Canada. How did these two groups view injustice? The group that felt trapped in Canada was less likely to blame inequality on a systemic flaw in their country. It seems that people trapped in a country—by policy or by poverty—are also likely to defend this same system that keeps them trapped.

It's an old debate: Does perfectionism lead to increased performance or does it sabotage the perfectionist? Researchers at the Canadian Dalhousie University found compelling evidence of the latter—psychology professors with perfectionist strivings had fewer journal articles, fewer citations, and were published in less prestigious journals than their messy-and-proud peers.

HOW TO STOP A PENALTY KICK

Gabriel Diaz COGNITIVE SCIENCE, UNIVERSITY OF TEXAS-AUSTIN

The average Premier League goalkeeper makes about $1.5 million a year. Chelsea keeper Petr Čech makes $145,000 a week. With cognitive scientist Gabriel Diaz's help, you can too (or at least you can dominate your adult rec league . . .). Working in Brett Fajen's lab at Rensselaer Polytechnic Institute, Diaz covered kickers and the ball itself with enough sensors to make any Hollywood special effects modeler proud. His thought was this: If you can turn the movements that create left shots and right shots into numbers, you can mine these numbers to see which movements best predict right or left ball direction. If you can spot these movements, you can increase the success rate of preemptive dives. And if you can increase the success rate of your preemptive dives, you can yacht the Adriatic Sea and stuff your mattress with dollars (or, see above comment about your adult rec league).

"The point at which the foot contacts the ball is almost 100 percent predictive of left or right," says Diaz. You'd expect that—where a cue ball hits a colored ball creates the colored ball's direction. And he confirmed soccer players' long suspicions that things including plant foot, upper leg direction, hips, and shoulders are moderately predictive.

"But more important," Diaz continues, "is that we found three sources of distributed information throughout the body that were quite reliable." A penalty shooter can lie with a plant foot or with shoulders, and so it's not statistically beneficial to watch any single body part. But keepers would do well to recognize combinations of these body parts—and this remains true even if a kicker points her plant toe left and kicks right. "What this does," says Diaz, "is bring about changes that cascade through other parts of the body—the distributed information network continues to forecast ball direction." Perhaps if you deceptively turn your plant foot left, in order to kick the ball right without falling over, some combination of your shoulders, hips, head, and kicking-side hand have to compensate hard right.

To find out if the Force is strong enough with keepers to

recognize these distributed information networks, Diaz played video of the networks in action—they looked like very coordinated marionettes made of the light points that Diaz originally captured with his sensors. In the video, the point-light marionette approaches the ball, swings body and leg, and just as the "foot" hits the "ball" the screen goes blank and subjects have to punch a left or a right button to predict the ball's direction. Fifteen of thirty-one subjects couldn't do it. But even in novices, sixteen of the thirty-one were able to beat chance when predicting penalty kick direction based on a kicker's overall body language during the approach.

So the moral for a trained goalkeeper, especially at a skill level at which kicks are almost assured to go hard into the right- or left-side netting, is to trust the Force. Stretch out with your feelings and trust their evaluation of Diaz's distributed information networks. The more you trust, the more you'll beat chance.

In their *Freakonomics* blog at the *New York Times*, Stephen Dubner and Steven Levitt point out that penalty kicks are beholden to game theory. Because most goalies guess, the best scoring strategy for a kicker is to blast the ball directly at the goalie's head—which won't be there at the point of contact because it's already in motion trying to stop a ball into the right or left netting. But kickers don't do this because, "If he misses to the right or left, the moment will be remembered more for the keeper's competence than for the kicker's ignominy," write Dubner and Levitt. Penalty kicks have the game theory payout shown on page 204.

How will a penalty kick be remembered?

	Open side	Keeper's side	Middle
Preemptive Dive	Nice shot	stunning Save	Idiot keeper
Wait & React	?	?	Idiot shooter

"Keep your eye on the ball!" Even if you've never played Little League, it's part of the cultural canon—do you hear it in your mind's ear when trying to finish a project, or swat a fly, or stay awake during a lecture? Well, Gabriel Diaz points to a study that suggests it may not be the best strategy after all. Michael Land and Peter McLeod tracked the eye movements of cricket batsmen and found that rather than keeping their eyes on the ball, the best batters picked up the ball only at specific points, and then made very quick and very accurate predictions about where to pick it up next. First they watched the release, then accurately ticked their eyes to where they knew the ball would bounce, then watched the bounce and the ball's trajectory about 100 to 200 ms after, then swung based on their prediction of time and position. The more ahead of the ball were their eyes—leaping from release to the predicted point of bounce—the better the batsman.

WORLD-RECORD PAPER AIRPLANE

Ken Blackburn AERONAUTICAL ENGINEERING, UNITED STATES AIR FORCE

Earning a world record allows paper plane designers to own football teams and date Russian oil heiresses. And according to aerospace engineer Ken Blackburn, current record holder and author of *The World Record Paper Airplane Book*, you need master only three things in your quest for paper plane glory: good folds, good throw, and good design.

Let's polish off the first two in a couple words: Good folds are extremely crisp, reducing the plane's profile and thus its drag. They also make the plane perfectly symmetrical. And a good throw means different things for different planes (we'll get into specs later), but for a world-record attempt, you use a baseball-style throw to launch the plane straight up, as high as possible—there's video of Blackburn's Georgia Dome launch and subsequent 27.6-second, world-record flight online at www.paperplane.org.

Now to design, wherein lies the true geekery of paper planes.

"Long, rectangular wings are for slow speeds and long glides, and short, swept-back wings are for high speeds and maneuverability," says Blackburn. You can see this in the difference between the condor and the swallow. The first is optimized for slow soaring, while the second—assuming an unladen European swallow—is optimized for quick dips and dives. You can also see these swept-back wings on the Space Shuttle, and because these high-speed wings have very little lift at low speeds, the Shuttle needs to keep an aggressive, nose-up angle of attack even when landing. A straight-winged Cessna can land almost flat to the runway.

These triangular wings certainly have a paper plane design purpose. "I make pointed airplanes myself," says Blackburn. "They certainly look cooler, and if you're just throwing a paper plane across the room, you might as well have something that looks cool."

But a world-record plane needs both the ability to act like a dart during launch, and like a glider after it levels off—a tricky balance. "People don't realize how desperately I would love to fold my plane the long way," says Blackburn, which would allow him to make wings from the 11-inch rather than 8.5-inch side of the paper. But so far he's been unable to find a design that has both long wings and the ability to withstand the force of the nearly 60 mph launching throw.

Wing shape defines other aspects of design too.

"For a rectangular, or nearly rectangular wing, the center of gravity should be a quarter of the distance from tip to tail," says Blackburn, "but for a plane with triangular wings, the center of gravity should be right at the midpoint." Basically, this is because the additional lift of a rectangular wing requires additional weight up front to keep the plane from pulling immediately nose-up and flipping instead of flying. "The further forward your center of gravity, the more your plane acts like a weather vane," says Blackburn. But you don't want to hang an anvil off the nose—that would negate the effect of lift. So optimal design is a balance between stability and lift.

Mathematically, it means that in a square-winged plane, you need exactly half the plane's weight right up front on the nose to make the full center of gravity rest a quarter of the way back. In the supersimple airplane below, it's easy to see that you want to fold exactly half the paper into the plane's leading edge.

Recreationally, you can adjust your paper plane's center of gravity with a paperclip. A cheater clip also helps ensure your plane's center of gravity remains below the wing, on the fuselage, making your plane stable right side up. But world-record rules disallow any additions to the paper and so creative folding is required.

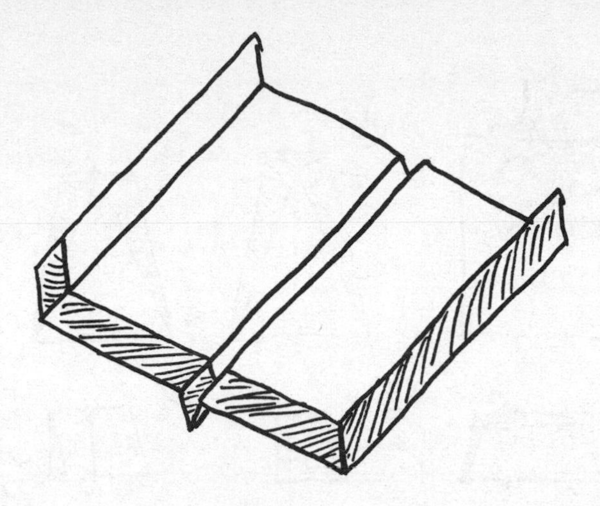

Instead of adding aerodynamically beneficial ballast, fold your wings slightly up, so that when you look directly at the plane's nose, the fuselage and wings form the letter "Y," not the letter "T" (horizontal wings) and certainly not like an upward-pointing arrow or three-line Christmas tree (downward angled wings).

Blackburn also gently folds up the wing's trailing edge to make his launchable dart a little more like a glider once it levels off. Flaps-up means that air pushes down on the trailing edge, slightly rotating the plane around its center of gravity and keeping the nose up. Like the Space Shuttle, which is forced to land with its nose high in the air, an increased angle of attack creates increased lift (as long as it doesn't make the plane flip).

Notice all these design features in the plans for Blackburn's world-record paper airplane, shown on the next page. But also notice that there might be room for improvement—can you lengthen the wings while still allowing a dartlike launch? If so, the paper plane world record and all its glory could be yours.

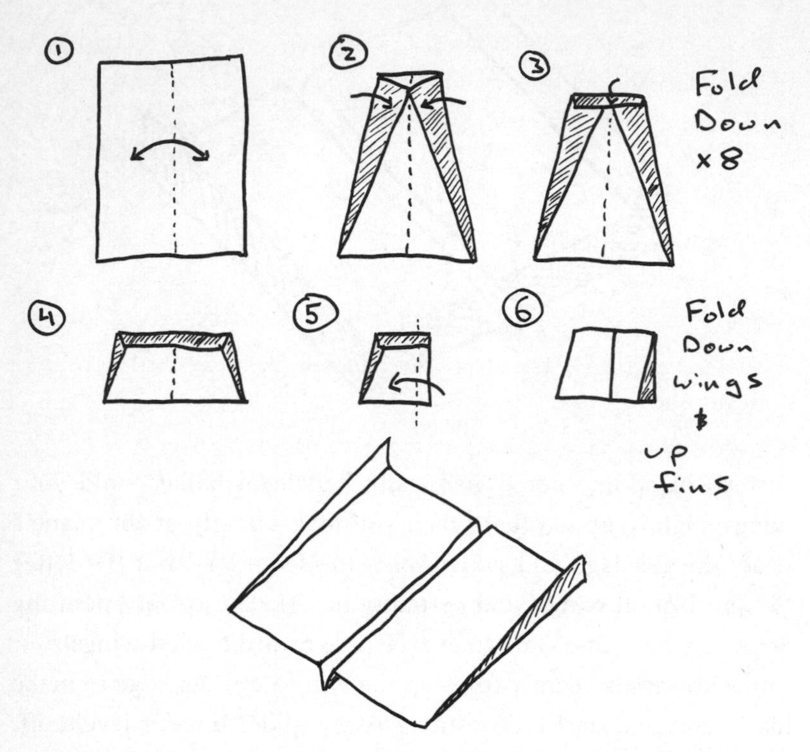

* From *The World Record Paper Airplane Book*, by Ken Blackburn

SUCCEED, YOU SLACKER!

Dolores Albarracin SOCIAL PSYCHOLOGY, UNIVERSITY OF ILLINOIS-URBANA-CHAMPAIGN

There are two kinds of people in this world: slackers and achievers. Achievers know how to spot slackers—they're the ones lounging by the lockers, collars turned up, sporting multiply pierced ears and asymmetrical smiles, listening to that new-fangled rock and roll music. And slackers know how to spot achievers—always on time and uptight, multiple sharpened pencils, taking notes as teachers blather on.

But do you know which one you are? Deceased Harvard researcher David McLelland saw the difference in tossers. He allowed subjects to choose the distance from which they tossed a ring at a post—people motivated by achievement picked a distance at which the task was tricky but not impossible, allowing them to succeed with effort and thus train their skills. People motivated by fun either chose close distances at which they could succeed every time, or impossibly far distances that required an entertaining, lucky throw to succeed. Do you push yourself at the gym (trying to lift ever heavier weights) or with your morning paper (you time the crossword)? If so, you're motivated by achievement rather than enjoyment.

OK, OK, social psychologist Dolores Albarracin of the University of Illinois points out that the difference isn't that stark—whether you're motivated by enjoyment or by achievement sits on a continuum, allowing you to hold both within you—maybe you have "6" motivation for fun and "8" motivation for achievement. But people sitting at different spots on that continuum are measurably different.

Albarracin showed this by testing fun/achievement motivation and then priming people with achievement words like *strive, attain, win, master,* and *compete*. Thus primed, achievers became even more motivated to achieve. But people naturally motivated by enjoyment rebelled against the priming and became even more motivated by fun.

In a follow-up, Albarracin showed that not only did this priming change attitudes, but it also changed behaviors. After again testing fun/achievement motivation and again priming subjects with achievement words, Albarracin plugged subjects into a word search task that she said was meant to measure verbal ability. Then the task was interrupted—blamed on computer problems—and after a couple minutes, subjects were given the choice to resume the word search task (achievement) or to switch to a cartoon rating task (fun). Primed achievers were more likely than unprimed achievers to go back to the word search. And fun-seekers primed with achievement words blew off the word search, defecting in droves to the cartoon task.

So making a fun-motivated person aware of an achievement context makes this person do even worse than he would naturally do. You can't push a slacker to succeed.

The reverse is true too: "If you frame a task as fun, achievers do worse," says Albarracin, "which is really depressing."

The implications are obvious: If you want fun-motivated students or workers (slackers!) to achieve, frame an activity as "so much fun!" rather than in the language of winning, losing, and striving. Likewise, if you know that you're one of these slackers and have a big project coming up, find a way to think of it as fun. If the task is simply horrible enough to preclude masking it with fun, Albarracin suggests using a "get your work done so you can play" mind-set. This allows fun to remain the goal, while ensuring slackers get their work done too.

Right now it's a beautiful, crisp fall day and I'd really like to wander downtown and pick up a used book and an ice-cream cone. Just five hundred more words and I'm out the door.

Albarracin found that the more a person believes they can defend an opinion from attack, the more likely the person is to change this same opinion in the face of contradictory evidence. Albarracin thinks it's likely that people with high "defensive confidence" have amassed these internal arguments as walls around a position they realize is weak.

THE SCIENCE OF SMOOTH OPERATING

Eastwick and Finkel SOCIAL PSYCHOLOGY, TEXAS A&M, NORTHWESTERN

Remember Finkel and Eastwick and their recommendations for speed dating success? Well, now they're all up in the grill of smooth operating. What, specifically, makes an initial romantic encounter smooth and what makes it awkward?

To answer the question, they and their colleague Seema Saigal gathered four-minute tapes of (independently rated) smooth and awkward first conversations between romantically inclined Northwestern University undergrads and then coded the behaviors they saw. As you'd expect, dates who exuded warmth and who were more focused on their dates than they were on themselves tended to create smoother conversations.

Interestingly, though, what mattered most beyond these obvious tools was not how prospective Romeos and Juliets acted but how they reacted. How does Romeo respond when Juliet quips and vice versa? The best responses (in addition to being warm and other-focused) walked a tightrope between too passive and too active. On the too passive side, Romeo might accept and agree with whatever Juliet says, exerting as much direction on the conversation as the proverbial limp-wristed wet towel. On the too active side, Juliet might drop Romeo's ball (as it were) and restart the conversation in an entirely new direction of her own choosing. (Of course, the worst thing a conversant could do is drop the ball entirely—withdrawing or failing to respond.)

The trick, according to Finkel, Eastwick, and Saigal, is to avoid extremes in autonomy. Accept your date's pass, redirect it slightly, and then return the ball—all with warmth and genuine interest in his or her responses.

This acceptance and redirection is the push and pull that creates smoothness.

The original smooth operating paper is surprisingly accessible and worth a read. You can find it easily with a quick search for "Finkel, Eastwick, Saigal."

There's a rich ecclesiastical, scientific, and popular literature exploring how people have sex. To wit: the *Kama Sutra* describes sixty-four sex acts across ten chapters; we know from fMRI images what sexual arousal looks like in the brain; and at any point we're but an unrestricted video search away from an online cornucopia (pornucopia?) of sex in action. But "one day my colleague David Buss and I were chatting and I said to him, 'Nobody's ever looked at *why* people have sex!'" says Cindy Meston, psychologist at the University of Texas–Austin, and author of the book *Why Women Have Sex.*

She and Buss rectified that: 1,549 undergraduates settled on 237 reasons for sex. Women listed as their top ten reasons: (1) I was attracted to the person; (2) I wanted to experience the physical pleasure; (3) It feels good; (4) I wanted to show my affection for the person; (5) I wanted to express my love for the person; (6) I was sexually aroused and wanted the release; (7) It's fun; (8) I was horny; (9) I realized I was in love; and (10) I was in the heat of the moment.

Men had the same top three, with numbers 2 and 3 switched. Lower in the top ten, men mix in "I wanted to achieve orgasm" and "I wanted to please my partner."

"The stereotype that men have sex for pleasure and women have sex for love is unfounded," says Meston. But while the top ten show significant overlap, distinctions emerge lower in the list. "Women don't have sex because they're in love," says Meston, "but because they're protecting love, stealing love, trying to create love, or doing it out of duty."

One participant said, "My mother taught me to have sex with my man or someone else will." Another said, "I'd rather spend five minutes having sex with him than listen to him whine and complain about how horny he is for the next two days."

WASH AWAY YOUR SINS

Norbert Schwarz SOCIAL PSYCHOLOGY,
UNIVERSITY OF MICHIGAN-ANN ARBOR

Have you ever tasted soap? It's not disgusting in the way you might imagine mashed worms or a yogurt cup of seagull guano could be. It's just sort of astringently chemical, olfactorily abrasive, and surprisingly long-lasting—the sensory equivalent of a spanking, which is how eating soap is commonly used. I know because in addition to chomping a bar of Dove for the purposes of this passage, I remember the taste well from my childhood.

Let's zoom out a click.

"Disgust is an evolutionary mechanism that ensures we don't touch corpses or feces, and if we do, we wash the affected body part afterward," says University of Michigan social psychologist Norbert Schwarz. And in Schwarz's opinion, morality co-opted this disgust pathway. Simply, immoral behavior provokes the same disgust as nastiness—Schwarz points to the vast majority of world religions that have rituals for washing away your sins. And so it stands to reason that if nastiness and immorality share a pathway, and if nastiness provokes the desire to wash, then so too should immorality provoke the same scrubophilia (now a word).

It's a nice story, but where's the evidence?

To find it, Schwarz designed a neat experiment. First, he asked subjects to imagine it's between them and another person for promotion in a law firm. The competitor has lost an important document and asks you to help her find it. Of course, there in your file cabinet you find the paper. What do you do now? In the ethical condition Schwarz had subjects call or e-mail the competitor and admit they'd found the doc. And in the unethical condition Schwarz had them lie (Sorry, haven't seen it!).

Subjects were told that was the end of the experiment. Oh, but with the extra time, would subjects mind filling out a quick product survey rating how likely they would be to purchase a range of products and how much they'd pay for them?

Subjects who lied in the law firm scenario said they were more likely to purchase Purell hand sanitizer and Scope mouthwash, and that they were willing to pay a higher price for those items. That's cool—immoral subjects wanted to wash—but it gets even cooler: Subjects who called the competitor and lied with their mouths wanted mouthwash, while subjects who e-mailed the competitor and lied with their fingers wanted hand sanitizer.

Not only does immorality provoke the same desire to wash as does nastiness, but it's just as body-part-specific.

Somewhere deep within your mother's evolutionary past, she knows that immorality of the mouth requires cleansing with soap. But sins are not the only things you can wash away with cleansers.

In another experiment, Schwarz explored the well-known phenomenon of postrationalization. Generally, if you rank your preferences for a list of ten things, in reality there's no distinction between numbers five and six—you could put either on top. But the act of choosing something over another—say, number five over number six—creates preference. In subsequent testing, you like number five much more than number six. In this way our brains create certainty from an uncertain world. Schwarz did something similar, but between the first preference ranking and the second test that shows the new, more distinct preferences, he had subjects either opine about antiseptic wipes or actually use the wipes. "Subjects who used the wipes literally wiped away their preferences," says Schwarz—it was as if they looked at the items anew, without ever having ranked them. Where there'd usually be a huge gap in preference between the object you previously chose and the object you previously spurned, after a quick swipe with an antiseptic wipe, subjects minds' were again open as the uncarved block.

Similarly, Schwarz had subjects gamble. Typically when people win a bet, they bet higher in the next round, and when they lose, they bet lower. (Thank you, irrational human psychology.) In his experiment, after the first round of betting, Schwarz gave half his subjects soap to smell and describe, and the other half actually used the soap to wash their hands. Just as with the antiseptic wipes, subjects who washed their hands with soap erased the effect of the previous win or loss—they didn't bet more or less the next round.

So not only is cleanliness next to godliness, but you can wash away the influence of your past, or "wash your hands of it." It's true of your past unsavory actions, irrelevant choices, and pointless experiences. If the past really isn't relevant to the future—or if you wish it weren't—a fresh start is only as far as your shower.

Out damn spot, indeed.

In another experiment, Schwarz's subjects passed an innocuous person in the hallway on the way to the study—half the time this innocuous plant sneezed, and half the time the plant just walked past. Perhaps it's not surprising that subjects who'd seen the sneezer estimated the risk of an average American catching a deadly disease as higher than subjects who hadn't recently been sneezed at. But what's cool is that their estimation of other risks increased as well—they thought it more likely to die of a heart attack or to be the victim of a violent crime. Schwarz called sneezing a "threat reminder," affecting perception of both relevant and irrelevant dangers.

GET MORE PLEASURE FOR LESS PRICE

Paul Bloom PSYCHOLOGY, YALE UNIVERSITY

There's a complex relationship between money and pleasure. On one hand, money is the measure of how much we like something—the more people like an object, the higher the price (price balancing supply and demand, and all that). And on the other hand, money can help create pleasure—if you're told that one bottle of wine is more expensive than another, you're likely to think the supposedly expensive wine tastes better.

That's no surprise.

But what is it, exactly, about the pricey wine that makes us like it more? Paul Bloom, Yale psychologist and author of the book *How Pleasure Works*, believes the pleasure we take from something is due not only to the brick-and-mortar thing itself but also to "an object's history—who created it, who's been in touch with it, our knowledge about the object." This is the item's essence or the ineffable qualities a thing carries with it, and is the root of sentimental value or irrational attachment. It's why artwork that sells for millions of dollars can lose almost all its value if it's proved to be a forgery. Yes, the object remains the same, but its essence changes.

Darn art snobs. Darn wine snobs.

But is snobbery really the mechanism that makes art and wine lovers care about a product's provenance? To study the effect of essentialism, Bloom and coauthor Bruce Hood brought children into the lab. Half brought with them a treasured object—a blanket, stuffed animal, etc.—and half brought with them toys which held no sentimental value. Then Bloom and Hood put kids' objects into what they told kids was a "duplication machine" that would use nifty science to create an exact duplicate of their toy. After "duplication" the researchers let kids pick which toy they wanted to take home, the original or the copy. Kids who brought nonsentimental toys tended to choose the copy, which was now coolified by science. Kids who brought attachment objects almost universally stuck with the original. That is, if they let Bloom and Hood put their attachment objects in the machine at all.

Despite (supposed) identical duplication, sentimental value didn't transfer and so kids stuck with their beloved items, which retained the value-added of their essence.

"We see the same phenomenon in adults," says Bloom. "We have objects in our lives that are valuable not because of what they're made of, but because of our attachment to them." For me, it's the baseball cards I have boxed in the garage. A complete set of 1986 Topps goes for $24.95 on Amazon, but I remember sorting these cards on the basement Ping-Pong table as a ten-year-old, checking off each number on a dot-matrix printout that ran from one to 792. I knew stats and values. I didn't let myself buy singles, instead hoping that in each pack I'd plug the gaps. (This is why I have bad teeth.) And despite the $24.95 price tag, I think I'd probably sell for a minimum $9,500. Any buyers?

Back to wine. What creates the very subjective pleasure we get from such luxury objects, and how can you get more of it? According to Bloom, "the more you work to get something, the more you'll enjoy it. Music is going to sound different if you know about it. The taste of food depends critically on what you think you're eating. Sexual arousal depends on who you think you're looking at."

Not only is knowledge power, but it's pleasure, too.

So if you want more pleasure from something, increase your knowledge about it. Of course, one critically important piece of information about wine is its price—a high price reflects others' votes for the wine being good. But if you have other information, you don't need price. Maybe you like pinot and you know that 2006 was a good year for Santa Barbara wine country. In that case, you wouldn't need price to tell you that a 2006 Babcock Pinot is a good wine. You'd pick it off even the bottom shelf and enjoy it just as much as if you'd had to ask the store manager to get it out from behind glass and then paid for it through the nose.

The same is true of absolutely anything—information creates essence, and essence creates pleasure. Does your spouse have a hobby you find completely inane? Learn about it to increase your own pleasure. If you just can't care about the difference between a Dogfish Head microbrew and Bud Light, take a brewing class. If you want to increase the pleasure of your vacation, learn about a place's essence—its history and culture.

Using knowledge rather than price to add essence means you can get more pleasure for less money.

Puzzle #18: Happiness at What Cost?

Jo makes $21.75/hr as a freelance medical transcriptionist. And let it be said that she also likes her wine. Every hour she spends learning about a bottle's origin (estate, winery, year, etc.) increases her enjoyment as much as buying a bottle half again the price of the first. How much must a bottle cost to make spending an hour learning about the wine a better buy than spending an hour working in order to buy a pricier bottle?

PUZZLE ANSWERS

1. MATH IS TOO SEXY

Start with mat = hematic

- Cancel "mat" leaving: 1 = heic
- Use $e = mc^2$ to get: $1 = H(mc^2)IC$
- Use $U = mgh$ to get: $1 = (u/mg)(mc^2)IC$
- Simplify: $mg = umc^2IC$
- Cancel "m" to get: $g = uc^2IC$
- Combine "c" to get $g = uc^3i$
- Write as: G = uccci

2. DR. STAT CRICKET PROP

In standard weather, the payout for a wager is the 1/46 chance of winning times the 46 payout, for exactly even money. Over time you break even. But in cold weather, Dr. Stat knows the chance of winning on each throw is 1/46 + 1/100 = 0.032. This times the 46 payout is an expected value of 1.46 times his money with each bet. If he bets $1,000 on one throw, that's an expected $1,460, and more than one hundred throws, that's $146,000. Of that total, $1,000 is his original bankroll, so he should expect to win $145,000.

3. MULTITASKING MIX AND MATCH

MIN	Task #1	Task #2
1	Get dressed	Check News
2		
3		
4		Fret
5		
6	Brush teeth	
7		
8	Make B'Fast	Coffee
9		
10		
11		
12		Read 4 Work
13	Eat B'Fast	
14		
15		
16		
17		Clean
18		
19		
20		

4. MATCHMAKER

The power pair of Jake and Emma is a red herring. Their bliss would force enough unhappiness on others that it's not worth allowing this match made in heaven. Instead, the pairs that create the highest overall happiness are John/Ella, Jeremy/Eliza, Jake/Eva, and Justin with the (apparently) effervescent Emma for a total of 51 preference points.

5. TRAMP TROUBLE

The biggest quadrant of the garage is the lower left, which is shown below, with a hypothetical trampoline. The question is, is the dotted line longer than 6 feet? Well, the dotted diagonal is the hypotenuse of a right triangle with sides of 5 feet and 4 feet. So $5^2 + 4^2 = (\text{Dotted line})^2$ and the dotted line is 6.4 feet long. Yes! The tramp will fit! Now let's hope the door to the house is on the right and not the left side of the garage.

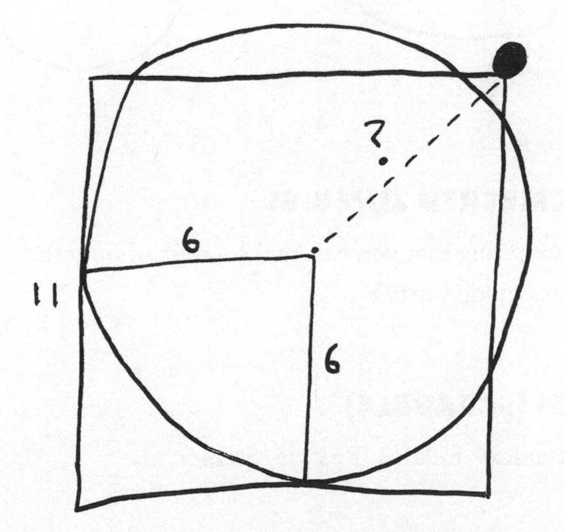

6. RACETRACK

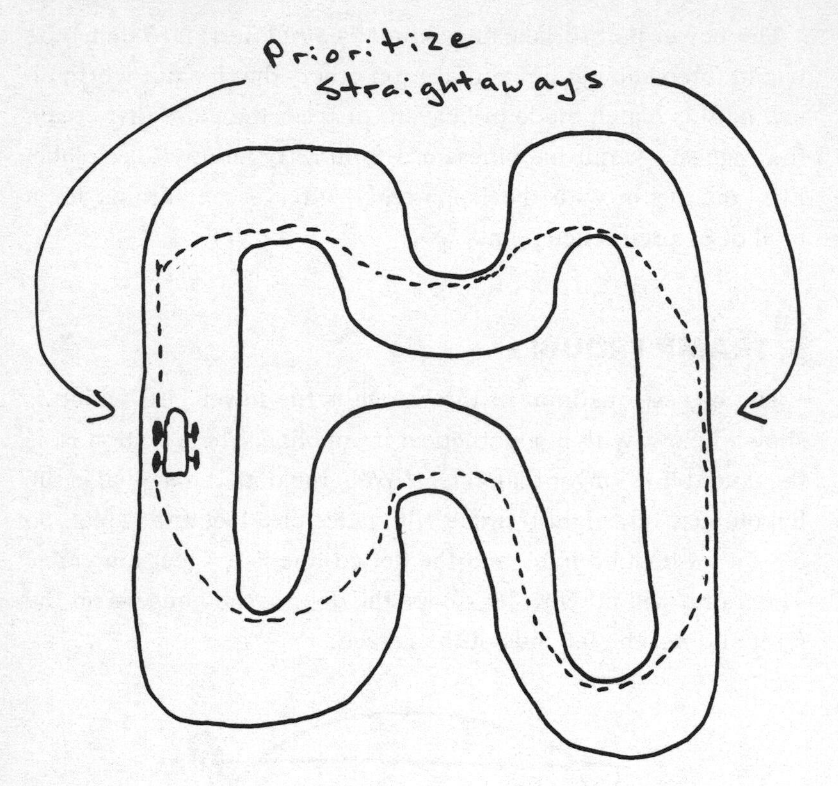

7. DISMEMBERED ZOMBIES

Isn't it frustrating that you can make a max of only three zombies from all these good parts?

8. BINGO! (SCRABBLE)

Elaters, Realest, Relates, Reslate, Stealer

9. BOOMERANG V. ZOMBIE

This is mostly a problem of conversions. It takes the zombie 6.09 seconds to cover the span (including the 2-second delay). And it would take the boomerang 6.42 seconds to return. If our hero runs, he reaches safety in 6.63 seconds. This looks bad all around, until you realize that the zombie also has to cover the extra distance to the tree, which takes it an extra 1.09 seconds. If the hero runs for the tree, he'll avoid the unwilling donation of his gray matter. (If you really want to bend your mind, imagine what happens if the hero runs toward the returning boomerang. . . .)

10. THE GOSSIP WEB

Here is one answer. There might be more.

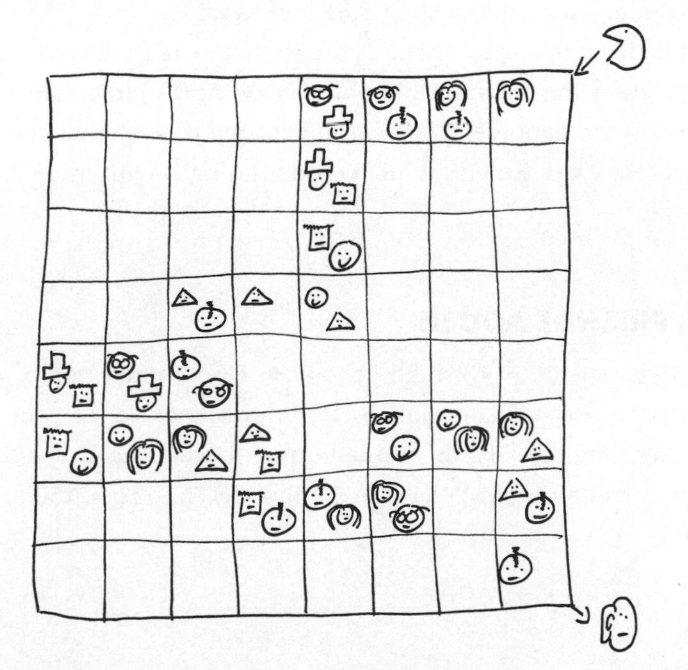

11. CAKE CUTTING

There are two fair ways to allocate the Batman. First imagine the cake as "points" combining volume with Batman—if B gets Batman, the cake is worth 168 total points, and if A gets Batman, the cake is worth 187 total points. And fair volume is B = 1.5A.

- So in the first case, A + 1.5A = 168. A gets 67.2 "points" of cake, and B gets 100.8 points of cake, of which 8 are due to Batman, so 92.8 in^3 of cake. Cutting the cake lengthwise, A gets a strip 3.36 inches wide, and B gets a strip 4.64 inches wide, including the Batman.
- In the second case, A + 1.5A = 187. A gets 74.8 points, of which 27 are due to Batman, so 47.8 in^3 of cake. B gets 112.2 points, all of which are due to cake. Cutting lengthwise, A gets a strip 2.29 inches wide including Batman, and B gets a strip 5.61 inches wide.
- But check this out: Giving A the Batman she so covets increases the overall value of the cake. And so to create maximum happiness, you should cut the cake so that she gets the Dark Knight, while compensating B with more cake.

12. FRIENDS ADD UP

Grade school = 13; high school = 13; summer camp = 13; college = 15; your first job = 15; grad school = 15; your kids' friends' parents = 17; an online fantasy football league = 17; and your current job = 32. 3(13) + 3(15) + 2(17) + 32 = 150.

13. A THREE-HOUR TOUR?

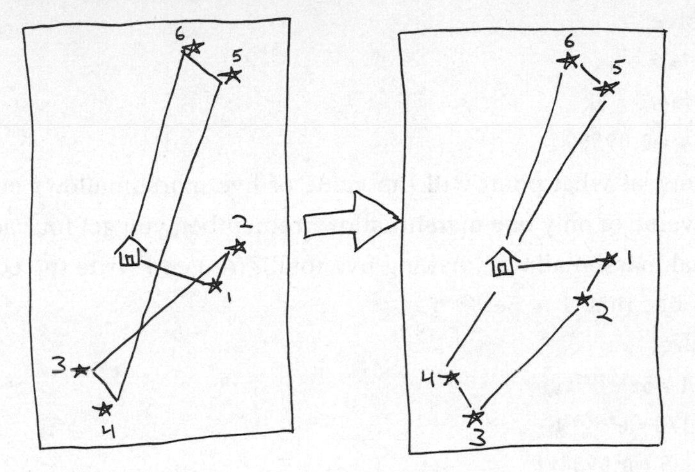

14. SCHOOLED BY FISH

Fish number 2 is a red herring (sorry . . .). Its personal connections are many but most of them are dead-end friends. Instead, fish numbers 9 and 11 are higher, with number 11's friends-of-friends-of-friends connections making it the winner, with a score of about 4.

15. TIME DISCOUNTING

The method is outed in the puzzle description—the "worth" of marshmallows at some point in the future is a problem of exponential decay, which uses the following equation:

(Remaining Amount) = (Starting Amount) e $^{\text{(Decay Rate x Time)}}$

Since marshmallows lose a quarter of their value every three minutes of wait time, 1 marshmallow will be worth only ¾ in

3 minutes. Plug these values into the equation for exponential decay to get this: $3/4 = 1e^{k3}$.

Solve:

- $3/4 = e^{3k}$
- $\ln 4/3 = 3k$
- $k = 0.09589$

Now, at what point will the value of five marshmallows equal the value of only one marshmallow (remember, you get four additional marshmallows, making five total)? You can write the equation like this: $1 = 5e^{0.09589}t$.

Solve:

- $1 = 5e^{0.09589}t$
- $1/5 = e^{0.09589}t$
- $\ln 5 = 0.09589t$
- $t = 16.78$ minutes

So the value of eating your initial marshmallow immediately is exactly equal to the value of eating five marshmallows 16 minutes and 47 seconds in the future. If you have to wait 20 minutes for the reward, you'd be better off immediately scarfing your first marshmallow.

Bonus question: How long do you have to make your decision before you're better off waiting for the additional four marshmallows at 20 minutes?

16. OCTOBER BOY

This is another twist on Martin Gardner's famous gender problem. Again, combining birth order with gender means with two kids you could have B-B, B-G, G-G, or G-B. Now, imagine the number of distinct possibilities with the calendar:

- If you first have a boy on a day containing a "1," you could have a boy or a girl second, on any of the 31 days, for a total of 62 possibilities, 31 of which are two boys. Cool.

- And the same is true if you second have a boy on a "1": 62 possibilities, of which half are boys. Only, 13 of these "new" possibilities aren't distinct. You already included boy-boy on every day containing a one. So instead of adding 62 more distinct possibilities, this adds only 49 new possibilities, of which only 18 are two boys.
- So add up all the possibilities for two boys: 31 + 18 = 49. And add up all possibilities: 62 + 49 = 111. There's a 49/111 = 0.44 probability that both kids will be boys.

17. MAP PROBLEM

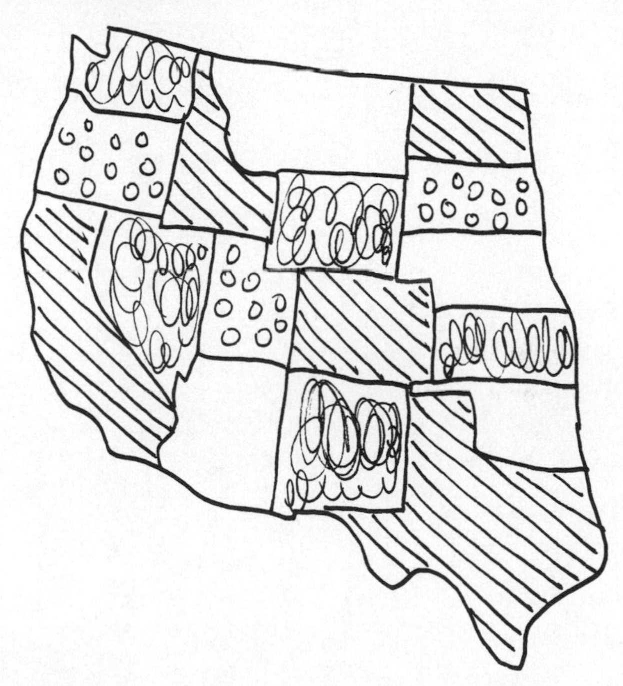

18. HAPPINESS AT WHAT COST?

A wine's "worth" is its cost multiplied by 1.5 times the hours Jo spends learning. That's not necessarily English. It's easier to write it as Worth = $1.5C_{ost}T_{ime}$. And if she spends the time working, the worth is the cost plus her pay, or Worth = $C_{ost} + 21.75T_{ime}$. Setting these equal (and working/studying for one hour) means $1.5C_{ost} = C_{ost} + 21.75$. Or $0.5C_{ost} = 21.75$. Or $C_{ost} = \$43.50$. For any bottle above that amount, Jo would be better off paying for increased worth by studying rather than working.

ACKNOWLEDGMENTS

Thanks to Julian and Jen, my spectacular editor and agent respectively. You continue to ensure I keep writing and that what I write isn't total pap. And again, thanks to the scientists included in this book and the ones I chatted with, but whose work I couldn't find a way to bastardize into the framework of a short, usable tip. Any offbeat humor and gerrymandering for practicality herein is a testament to these scientists' willingness to both perform the world's greatest science and then allow it to be humanized in a way that makes it seem the stuff of offhand dinner-party conversation. Humor aside, I'm humbled by the opportunity to punch into your world, if however briefly. And my wife, two kids, and Labrador haven't yet thrown me out on my ear after hearing yet another totally fascinating conversation recapped over the breakfast table, and for that they deserve not only thanks but medals. And thank you, whoever bought this book! Because of you, I am right now basking on my yacht off the Croatian coast, eating salty caviar and sipping wine of a year whose digits sum to something other than three or four. Or I am at least in the backyard shed insulated with cardboard that is my office, watching in the early morning as hot-air balloons rise from Boulder and squirrels mate on the back fence, while planning my next book. Cheers.

About the Author

GARTH SUNDEM is the bestselling author of *Geek Logik, The Geeks' Guide to World Domination,* and *Brain Candy.* You can find him at garthsundem.com, as the bimonthly puzzlemaster at *Wired*'s *GeekDad* blog, at TED.com, and/or by using a searchlight to broadcast the periodic table of the elements into the night sky (or by baking berry pie). Garth and his wife live in Colorado with their two kids and a large Labrador.

ALSO BY
GARTH SUNDEM

Tastier than a Twizzlers yet more protein-packed than a spinach smoothie, *Brain Candy* is guaranteed to entertain your brain! These delicious and nutritious pages are packed with cutting-edge brain science, puzzles and paradoxes, and eye-opening perception tests and hacks.

BRAIN CANDY

$14.00 paper (Canada: $17.00)

978-0-307-58803-6

Sorry, beautiful people. These days, geeks rule the world. And here is the book no self-respecting geek can live without—a guide jam-packed with 314.1516 short entries exploring the essential joys of science, pop-culture trivia, paper airplanes, pure geekish nostalgia, and much, much more.

THE GEEKS' GUIDE TO WORLD DOMINATION

$13.95 paper (Canada: $15.95)

978-0-307-45034-0

Available wherever books are sold